A Ghostly Road Tour of
Michigan's Upper Peninsula

Jan Langley

Jan Langley (signature)

Written by Jan Langley

Cover and Interior Design by Stacey Willey

Cover Illustration, Original Oil Painting by Sandi Mager

Edited by Roslyn Mcgrath and Patricia Utzman

Copyright 2006
Jan Langley

Published by Captain and Harry L.L.C.
Escanaba, Michigan

Publishing Coordination by
Globe Printing, Inc.
Ishpeming, Michigan

ISBN 978-0-9724777-1-0
ISBN 0-9724777-1-3

First Printing January 2007

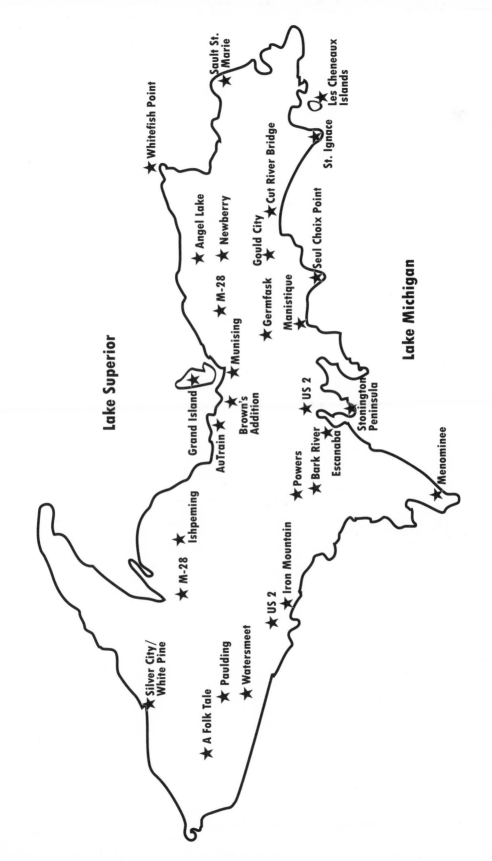

Table of Contents

"The times have been that, when the brains were out, the man would die, and there an end; but now they rise again."

~ *Macbeth*

Introduction

We have been programmed from an early age not to believe in ghosts, yet we must accept what our eyes have seen and our ears have heard after eliminating all other possible explanations. I had never believed in ghosts, spirits, or specters of the phantom world. Not that I didn't want to. I believe we all have an interest in things that "go bump in the night." I believe we all like to be … somewhat scared. We like to feel those chills that go up and down our spine and create goose bumps on our arms when we encounter that "something" that takes us into the realm of the supernatural.

I have discovered in my research that you don't have to see a ghost to experience a ghostly presence. Spirits make themselves known in many different ways. A spirit can be a shadow on a wall that slips down the hallway or an apparition that follows the same path every day at the same time and often on a certain date, like a tape recording. A spirit may be footsteps on the stairway, or the smell of your mother's favorite perfume. An inexplicable fog, the ringing of a bell, the turning of the pages in a book, or the disappearance of an item–all of these may all signal the presence of something paranormal.

Do any of these occurrences offer scientific proof of the spirit world? We have to ask what ghost would allow itself to be caught and examined in a controlled environment? Often their misty presence can only be felt, and how do you examine a feeling? The people who have shared their experiences with me for this book fully believe what they have recounted. Some have told their stories to me boldly, without fear, almost laughingly. Others have told their stories with fear in their eyes and a cautionary look over their shoulder. I have researched each haunting encounter that appears in these pages to the best of my ability. I do not offer explanations for the stories I have investigated and the things I have heard and seen. Have I been frightened? You bet. There are places I will not return, nor spend the night ever again. Is there evil? Yes, I believe so, in some instances. However, the harmless, benevolent spirits like that of Captain Townshend at the Seul Choix Point Lighthouse far outnumber the smells of evil.

Remember, first and foremost, I am a story teller, a teller of tales. So, I leave you now to search out the truth in the following stories told to me by the people of the Upper Peninsula, known for their spirit of adventure and hardy souls. A special thanks to each and every one who had the courage to share with me the tales they kept from their friends and neighbors for fear of being called "crazy." A note of caution: be careful in which establishments you choose to spend a night or dine as you begin your ghostly tour of the Upper Peninsula.

Note the orbs in this photo of an abandoned house in the U.P.

Seul Choix Point Lighthouse, Gulliver

We begin our journey into the spirit world at Seul Choix Point Lighthouse. The lighthouse hauntings have been featured on Fox Family TV Network, Lifetime TV Network and investigated by several paranormal research groups. Outstanding in this type of research is the Upper Peninsula Paranormal Research Society. It has issued a tantalizing investigative report about Seul Choix on it's website: www.UPPRS.org. The following is a true account of my own experiences.

I had no interest in investigating haunted places or searching for the supernatural until I met Marilyn Fischer in the fall at an auction in Manistique, Michigan. She mentioned she was the president of the Gulliver Historical Society and that it was in the process of

restoring the Suel Choix Point Lighthouse. Located on the shore of Lake Michigan, about eight miles south of Gulliver, the lighthouse had remained in continuous service until the US Coast Guard installed an airport beacon light in the tower. It was then abandoned in 1973. Since that time, it had fallen into a sorry state of disrepair.

In 1987, the newly formed historical society pledged to restore and preserve the lighthouse. When I expressed an interest in the project, Marilyn invited me down to see what they had accomplished. She also offered to introduce me to the ghost of Captain Joseph W. Townshend. "… although, the Captain isn't our only ghost, " she continued, " he is the most active."

Ghosts, I thought. *Phooey!* I considered myself much too bright for that kind of nonsense. The lighthouse was closed to tourists for the season, so setting a date and time to meet was easy for both of us.

As I drove up to the old lighthouse that late fall morning, for some strange reason I felt as if I had come home. I don't know why. I wasn't a lighthouse collector or even very interested in lighthouses. Marilyn was waiting for me on the back porch of the lighthouse residence. As I approached she said, "I saw something rolling down the porch when I walked up the sidewalk a few minutes ago. I thought it was a pencil. It came from the back door all the way to the steps in a perfect straight line. Then it rolled down the steps, one at a time, to where I was standing."

She looked to see my reaction as she held it in her hand." It's a cigar. Captain Townshend smoked cigars," she remarked quietly." There's not even a hint of a breeze today. How can a cigar roll down the steps without any wind?" She held it up to look at it again, then put it in her pocket. "Come on in, Jan," she said, as she unlocked the back porch door. Little did I realize that as that door opened, a whole new world was opening to me.

The lighthouse was warm and welcoming. I felt very comfortable and "at home." The historical society was doing a wonderful job of restoration. The original woodwork and floors were polished to perfection. My personal tour began as we walked down the hallway, past a staircase that gleamed in the sunlight, to the kitchen where Marilyn told me about the old wood stove,

cupboards and utensils that were used in the late 1800's.

She then smiled innocently as she placed her hands on the back of one of the four kitchen chairs. "This table belonged to Captain Joseph Willy Townshend who was keeper of Seul Choix from 1901 until his death in an upstairs bedroom on August 10, 1910. We found the table in four pieces in four separate corners of the basement about seven years ago."

As I walked around the table, I could smell the sweet pungent odor of a good cigar. I ignored it as she continued, "Everything had been fine up until that day, Jan. It was after we put the table together and put it here in the kitchen that things began to happen."

"Things?" I questioned.

She smiled again and said, "Yes, like the cigar smoke you smell right now. Captain Townshend's wife wouldn't let him smoke his cigars in the house back then, but she's not here anymore … is she?" Her cheeks dimpled as she led me into the dining room. I admit somewhat of a chill ran up my spine as I followed her. The table in here was set for eight dinner guests. Sparkling silverware and wineglasses complemented the place settings. An old buffet stretched along the end wall. Pictures of even older people in oval frames watched us.

Marilyn stood leaning against the buffet as I paused to look at a sewing mannequin dressed in a light keeper's uniform. In a soft voice that was almost a whisper, she identified the assortment of small photographs, cups, saucers and jewelry that filled the small cupboard next to me. I commented on the beauty of the room and how warm and appealing it felt to me as I joined her next to an antique buffet. There was a Bible at one end and a silver tea service centered beneath a picture of an older man with a white beard and haunted eyes.

A picture of Captain Townshend, "with a white beard and haunted eyes."

She noticed my glance and said, "That's Captain Townshend. He really isn't as frightening as he looks." She ran her hand gently over the leather cover of the Bible. "This," she said, "was donated by the descendents of Captain Townshend. When we were in here cleaning out the spiders and dead bats last spring, it slammed shut with such force we thought it was going to go through the top of the buffet. None of us were anywhere near it. The Captain doesn't like spring cleaning." She spoke softly over her shoulder as we left the room to enter the parlor. I couldn't help but feel my skin crawl as I hurried to keep up with her. We continued through the parlor without incident.

It was hot that day with not a breath of wind. Some people call this time of year Indian Summer. I suddenly felt tired and headachy." Marilyn, can we take a break?" I asked. I was still smoking at that time and felt the need for nicotine badly.

"Sure" she replied as she led the way to the back porch and a wooden bench that looked to be a hundred years old.

"So tell me, Marilyn…," I said as I lit up a cigarette and

inhaled deeply. "… you mentioned when you found the table, things began to happen. What did you mean by things?" At that moment I heard the tinkling of a bell and watched the back door gently open and close. A sudden gust of wind slammed the outer screen door back on its hinges. Then, all was quiet again.

"Do you believe in ghosts, Jan?" she asked.

"I don't know," I replied. "I don't know that I would blame that door thing just now on ghosts."

"I do," she replied, "and I think you will too. Why don't you plan on spending a week in one of the cottages at Old Deerfield and we'll go ghost hunting after I'm done with work at night. Or are you a Sissy Girl?" she laughed.

My tour continued without further incident.

With deer season and the holidays fast approaching, we couldn't get together but for short visits until the following spring. Inspired by my visit that day to the lighthouse, I spent the winter writing my first children's book, *The Captain and Harry, a haunting tail of Seul Choix Point Lighthouse*. I made reservations for a cabin at Old Deerfield for the second week in June.

At that time, Marilyn and her husband Glen were the owners of the Old Deerfield Resort. There was a restaurant and twenty-eight cabins strung along Gulliver Lake like a necklace. Marilyn was waiting for me on the steps of the restaurant as I drove up. "Drive down to cabin 17, Jan. It's on the left. I'll follow you," she called to me.

Cabin 17 sat on the shoreline. I unpacked the Jeep, popped open a can of Pepsi and waited for Marilyn to join me at the picnic table under a huge pine tree.

We had become good friends during the past few months and giggled and laughed like teenagers as we laid out our plans for the week. She told me some of the stories of the Captain's latest activities at the lighthouse. "He really doesn't like spring cleaning and he lets that fact be known every spring. Lights go on and off, bells ring, and last week one of the state troopers, who had come down to investigate after the alarm system went off, told us he heard voices in the kitchen and sounds like chairs being moved. But when we entered through the locked doors, we found nothing. The chairs circled the table, neatly in their places. There was a fork lying across one of the plates. That's a quite common occurrence at the lighthouse. It is a habit the Captain brought with him from England, that is, laying his fork upside down on his plate. Then there is the cigar smoke that will permeate an area for an instant or two and then, just as quickly, dissipate into nothing. The chairs often do move, as do plates and cups. Just this past week, two tour guides have seen his spirit standing in an upstairs window holding the curtain back. Throughout this spring, several times the tour guides have reported seeing foggy images of people in the large round mirror in an upstairs bedroom… his bedroom," she murmured.

"Images of what?" I asked.

"Spirits," she replied. Grandma saw a woman in a wedding gown with flowers trailing down the front of the dress. She couldn't see her face. Jim told us he saw the Captain himself. He saw his faded face with his piercing eyes and white moustache. Maude has told us she has seen an older woman who looked like one of the Goudreau women."

My first encounter with Captain Joseph Willy Townshend came that very evening. Marilyn and I drove the pick-up from Old Deerfield to the lighthouse. We passed an old Indian cemetery filled with bones and spooky stories, the kind that scoutmasters tell kids on camping trips. I was startled to see a flashing light over the treetops in the midst of a pitch-black night without stars or moon. As we pulled around a curve, I could see it was the lighthouse beacon. My heart thudded just a little as I saw the outline of the lighthouse tower in the darkness.

"That's funny," said Marilyn, "the parking lot lamp is out. The tour guides must have forgotten to turn it on when they left. We'll have to go down to the basement and turn it on. Do you mind, Jan?"

Mind? Me mind? Go down in the dead of night into the basement of a dwelling that, by all indications of everyone I had spoken to about Suel Choix Point Lighthouse, was haunted? Mind? Yes, I minded. I didn't say a word. She gave me that "Marilyn grin" as we followed her flashlight beam down the walkway to the porch by the lighthouse tower. It was a quiet night. In the distance, I could hear the gently lapping of waves against the rocky shore. We entered the lighthouse residence through the back door. Although I put on a good front for Marilyn, I was hesitantly scared. Do you know what I mean by hesitantly?

She switched on lights as we passed the stairs to the upper bedrooms, including, the bedroom where the Captain had died. The bedroom where the strange mirror was located and its haunting images. The same stairs where many people have seen the Captain leaning on the banister. We continued our way to the door that led to

An ectoplasm forming in the Captain's bedroom. An ectoplasm is believed to be an energy which is undetectable by the naked eye, but shows up on film.

the basement. The hair on the back of my neck stood straight up as I followed Marilyn as closely as possible, without being indecent, down the curved stone steps. The basement lights were not working. It figures, I thought to myself. She turned the switch on and off several times. Nothing. Goose bumps marched down my arms.

"Come on, this way," Marilyn said as the flashlight slid across stone-lined walls." They embalmed the Captain here," she whispered as she pushed the flashlight beam over the massive stone sinks we were passing.

"What do you mean, embalmed him?" I asked.

"They drained his blood from him and then filled his body cavity with salt."

"You're kidding me, right?" I answered.

The flashlight beam slipped up some stone steps. "They carried his body up these cellar steps to the casket and the wagon that waited outside." By this time I was clinging to the back of her shirt and walking with shuffling steps as I followed her, hoping I wouldn't see anything in the surrounding darkness. The dark, menacing corners of the basement crouched in waiting for me. *Please, please, don't let anything show up down here,* I thought to myself.

"Here, Jan, hold the flashlight for a minute. Aha, here's the switch and it's … on? What the heck … it must be burned out." She flicked it on and off several times. "Well, I better keep it on off. I am always so worried about a short in the wiring down here." One more time she pulled the handle into the off position.

I breathed easier as we reached the top of the stairs and overhead lighting that reached into the dark corners and angles of the main floor rooms.

"Are you here tonight, Captain Townshend?" Marilyn whispered as we paused in the hallway.

I must have jumped a mile. I grabbed her arm." Where is he? Can you see him?" I exclaimed.

"No," she laughed, " I can't see him but I can sense ... something. Let's go to the kitchen." I sat at the kitchen table and looked up at the fan the historical society had installed that early spring. Its slight breeze felt wonderful on my sweaty forehead. Marilyn continued to share with me more details of the Captain's death as she leaned against the wall length side cupboard. If, I thought, this place is really haunted by the Captain, I wonder what he thinks of the addition of a modern fan?

At that moment, I smelled the cigar smoke. Strong. "Marilyn ... do you smell it?"

"Yeah."

"It's gone now."

"It does that. Comes and goes in an instant."

I felt goose bumps chase each other across my arms and legs. They were getting to be old friends. I looked at Marilyn. She was standing up at attention, beads of perspiration formed on her forehead. And then, again, cigar smoke permeated the air. Marilyn started to shake all over. I reached for her and grabbed her hand. A frigid wall of air circled us. My spine was ice and chills covered my hands and legs. Suddenly, the cigar smoke was gone. So was the coldness and Marilyn was herself again.

"What was that all about? What happened to you?" I anxiously questioned.

"I could see him, Jan, over there by the back door. He just stood there watching us."

I don't know why I did what I did next, but I leaned over to the kitchen window and looked out at the darkened lamp. "If you are here, Captain Townshend, blink twice." It did. Twice. Like the headlights of an oncoming semi-truck. I fell back against the table.

"My God," said Marilyn." He has just given you proof that he is here. He must approve of you."

Great, I thought. That's just great. A ghost likes me. Just my luck. My heart was pounding wildly.

"I think that's enough for tonight, Jan. Are you ready to go?" she asked quietly.

Was I ready? My hands were shaking and my legs felt like rubber bands. Was I ready to go? oh yeah "Uh huh," I said out loud, shaking my head yes.

Our conversation was limited as we drove back to Old Deerfield. When I opened the door of the truck, Marilyn asked, "So, Jan, now do you believe in ghosts?

I leaned back in the seat. I looked up at the stars that had finally decided to puncture the darkness of the night." A little bit more than I did yesterday," I answered.

The following day she called to let me know an electrician had checked the switches. What we saw was impossible, he told her. There was no power to that area at all that night.

That was the beginning of a summer of introductions to the ghost of Captain Joseph Willy Townshend. Doors moving, ghostly fogs on the grounds of the lighthouse, dead camera batteries, and ghostly images in the mirror of the dead Captain's bedroom have made me a firm believer in ghosts. The experiences at the lighthouse that summer piqued my curiosity to investigate other ghostly tales.

The following stories are those I have investigated through interviews and research over the past several years. Please join me on a ghostly road tour of Upper Michigan, and make sure to include a visit to the haunted Seul Choix Point Lighthouse

Jolly Inn, Germfask

I had a call from the owner of the Jolly Inn, located in Germfask, that the bar and restaurant were being haunted. I decided to go ahead with a short jaunt down the peninsula in spite of severe thunderstorm warnings for the entire U.P. Normally the weather forecasts for the U.P. don't mean a lot. They are usually wrong. As luck would have it that day, thunder and lightning pursued me all the way from Blaney Park to the small spot in the road called Germfask. My destination, the Jolly Inn, was on the highway that continued up to Seney. As I pulled into the Inn's side parking area, I wondered how anyone could live this far away from the rest of the world. It was dead center in the middle of the Upper Peninsula. Winters here must be absolute hell, I thought to myself as thunder rolled around me and bounced off the forest of jack pines that populated the area. A perfect place for a haunting, *I thought as I left the car.*

Friday Night Special - all you can eat
Whitefish & Walleye $7.99   or   Perch $8.99
Includes soup and salad bar

"The Friday night special" sign greeted me as I opened the old-fashioned screen door and let it slam behind me as a huge clap of thunder boomed. I felt goose bumps walk up my arms and across the back of my neck as my eyes adjusted to the darkened bar. Carol, the present owner of the Jolly Inn, greeted me, "So did you feel a chill as you walked in?" She was sitting on a bar stool, legs crossed, smoking a cigarette.

"Most people do, when they first come in. Could be 90 degrees out. Doesn't matter. Most of them still get a chill. It's just our ghost's way of saying hello." She stuck out her hand and continued, "Hi, I'm Carol. You must be Jan. Come on with me. I'll give you the grand tour."

I turned on my miniature tape recorder, grabbed my camera and followed her through a doorway that led to a long set of wooden stairs. "This is where the most activity takes place," she said as she led the way up the back stairs hidden behind the wall of the bar. They creaked at every movement. Lightning flashed through the window at the top of the steps as I followed her. The old wooden banister wiggled under my tight grasp.

"Jake Jolly built the place in November of 1937. He is our ghost. He has been haunting this place for years," she remarked. "This is the room that most of the sounds come from." It was a room about 12' x 12' with a full-sized bed in one corner and a small dresser in the other. Next to the bed, a small pink lamp sat on a table. An ashtray balanced on the edge nearby.

She continued, "We hear footsteps up here all the time. Back and forth, like someone is pacing. And see that door," she pointed at the door opposite the bed. "That door keeps opening and closing. The girls, (waitresses) often come up here to lay down for a break, or in case of bad weather, some have had to spend the night. Some of the girls won't even come up here anymore. I finally had a latch put on it. I have sat here on the bed and watched as the latch slowly moved and unlocked the door. I had to spend the night here one night because of a storm. I shouted, 'Jake Jolly, you stop it right now! You're scaring the wits out of me!' The door stayed closed after I gave him hell."

Lightning spread its fingers through the room as she continued.

"Yes, Jake Jolly is our ghost." She led the way down the stairs. Thunder clapped as we reached the bottom. "It's had several owners since it was built. Some stayed for a few years; others didn't last a few months.

Do you want something to drink?" she asked as she led the way back into the bar.

"No," I replied. Once again goose bumps troubled me. I climbed on a barstool and waited while she grabbed a Coke and lit another cigarette.

"I worked here three years before we bought the place so my husband and I are well acquainted with the antics of Jake. I know he's harmless. My wait staff doesn't like it though. Some have stayed with me in spite of his pranks, but many have left. That's one of the reasons why I'm short-handed tonight," she explained. "We had a washing sink put in the kitchen. It worked just fine for over a month. This morning the health inspector came; the water would not come on. We jiggled and turned, but no water. My husband finally looked underneath to discover the shut-off valve was turned off. I swear we never even knew it was there. One of my waitresses was watching the whole business. She said that it was the last straw for her. She isn't coming back."

"Boy, that storm is really kicking up, isn't it?" I could now hear the wind blowing through the trees as thunder smashed again. Lightning cracked very close. The power went out.

"Stay there, Jan," Carol said. "I'll get some candles."

That left me alone …in the dark … in a storm … in a place that's haunted. I saw the candle glow before I saw Carol. Suddenly the lights came on again.

She laughed. "We always lose power in a storm." She took a deep breath and let it out slowly as she continued.

"I guess the only time I was really scared was one day while I was waiting for the grill to cool down. One of the men working for us asked me if Joe was around. I told him I had seen him in the backyard cleaning out a shed earlier. He told me he heard noises back in the cooler as he entered the kitchen and thought it might be Joe. He went back to check. I heard him shout, 'Come here! Hurry up! My God! Hurry!' I ran to the cooler where he held the door open and there in the air was a ten pound bag of macaroni flying in a circle. Macaroni was shooting from it and hitting the ceiling and walls and rolling across the counters. Macaroni was everywhere. We slammed the door shut. We locked up the bar and went home. It took me several days to return to work. My husband just laughed."

She led me into the kitchen to show me the cooler. It was a normal cooler. She said when they cleaned, they still found macaroni behind the shelves.

As we walked to the dining room, she told me about the many times that she had locked the kitchen door. It has a dead bolt. It still opened no matter how many times it had been closed. As we passed the waitress station, she told me about the can of hair spray that refused to stay on the shelf. A waitress, Judy, replaced it three times. She watched it get pushed off the shelf three times. She finally got tired of it falling and put it in a bowl. Judy told me, if it hops out of there one more time, she was out of here. Judy is also the gal that has seen Jake in the dining room.

Carol walked to the dining room entrance from the kitchen. "Right here," she said. "Judy was cleaning the shelves where the cups are when out of the corner of her eye she saw a man with a light-colored shirt and dark trousers walk through this doorway and into the kitchen. She came into the kitchen after a few minutes to get some towels and asked me where the guy went that she had just seen. I told her no one had come into the kitchen."

The lights dimmed, came on again, dimmed again and went

out. "Damn! Stay here, Jan, I'll be right back with the candles again."

I stayed right there, looking in the direction of Judy's apparition. Thunder climbed the walls and wind pushed at the side door. The lights came on before Carole returned. I felt a chill on the back of my neck and slowly turned to face the bolted back door.

"Damn storm," said Carol as she re-entered the room. My heart banged against my chest from being startled. "Over there," she pointed toward the parking lot windows, "is where I saw our ghost dressed in a light-colored shirt and dark pants. I was coming from the kitchen and going into the bar. He was standing by that table by the window. He just melted away."

I wasn't scared until I thought about it. I needed a cup of coffee. My palms were sweaty. Thunder clapped against the back of the building and rattled every dish on every shelf in the place. Carol brought the coffeepot over to one of the dinning room tables and poured us both a cup of the steaming liquid. It smelled wonderful. She put two candles on the table and lit them both.

"Just in case," she smiled. "So, what do you think? Are we being haunted?"

"Have you had any kind of electrical problems, other than during storms?" I asked.

"Yes, in fact, we have and if we sit here long enough, we might get to watch one of his tricks."

"In here? The dinning room?"

"You bet" she replied "notice that we have nice globe lights in the ceiling. First, one will go out. I'll get a new bulb for it. Then a few days later, the second one will go out. I'll put a new bulb in that one. Then the third one will go out; same story until this has gone all around the room, one after another. It might be a month or two before it starts all over again."

I finished my coffee and watched the lightning make patterns across the tables and chairs. I glanced up at the lights around the room. "When's the last time it happened?" I asked.

"About a month ago," she said as she asked me to follow her back into the bar. I brought along my coffee and took a sip.

Thunder rippled from a long way off. The storm was heading toward Newberry. It was time I headed home. I gathered my notes as Carol told me about the morning that she opened the door to pure havoc. Bar stools were in disarray, ashtrays, tables, everything in the bar room had been scattered like leaves. She called her daughter thinking there had been a party after closing the night before. Her daughter told her absolutely not. Everything was fine when she had left. The door hadn't been broken into, nothing was missing; the only explanation was Jake Jolly.

Is the Jolly Inn haunted? I believe it is and I also believe this spirit is old and powerful. It takes a lot of energy to materialize and even more to move things as large as furniture.

When I went back to the Jolly Inn on a night in early September for the Friday night fish fry, I noticed one of the lights was burned out in the dining room and the second one was dimming. There was an old man sitting by the door wearing a light colored shirt and dark pants. I didn't ask who he was. I didn't want to know.

By the way, I highly recommend the Friday Night Fish Fry!

The Jolly Inn in Germfask

The Reunion, Gould City

I received a call late in October to meet with a gentleman who told me the following story. He has since passed away. I repeat it here in my own words from the notes I jotted down that day. I have used my imagination to fill in the blanks.

Like most people who have been born in the Upper Peninsula, Ken often returned home on the Fourth of July for the annual family reunion held at a large camp near Gould City. I can remember him telling me it was one of those rare, warm, sunny days in the U.P. as campers, trucks, and cars filled with relatives arrived at the old log cabin. Greetings were called out from family to family and a feeling of celebration was in the air.

He remembered that Uncle Charlie gathered the younger kids to pick up kindling for the campfire that would be the center of the evening's fun. Aunt Edna and Aunt Clara, along with Aunt Louise, Aunt Estelle and some of the daughters and cousins, went into the kitchen to plan the meals for the next few days. Tents were set up, camping trailers balanced, and water jugs from the old well were filled to the brim. Mosquito netting was hung from the porch ceiling with only a slit left to walk through. Jars lined the old porch railing for the youngsters to catch fireflies. Bright sunlight filtered through the tall jack pines and cast reflections across the water of the inland lake next to the cabin. It was a beautiful time of year and it was good to be together again.

Night settled in quickly after a camper's buffet was spread out on picnic tables surrounding the firepit. Most of the younger kids were zipped into sleeping bags that lined the front porch from which occasional giggles burst forth, but as the evening wore on, they grew into the silence of tired sleep. Crickets chirped and an owl let them know he was near and watching. It was about then, with the fire slowly burning into red coals, that Aunt Gladys brought out her photograph album. Soon all the families had spread out their albums across the tables.

This too was a ritual, as they all sat and poured over the books with "remember-whens" A full moon soon joined the gathering.

"Doesn't Grandpa look young in these pictures?" asked Mary, one of Gladys' daughters.

"He looks young in all of the pictures," answered Kelly.

"I'm not sure if I should ask," Mike hesitated, "but have any of you ever had something funny happen to you after he died?"

"What do you mean, 'funny'?" asked someone at the end of the table.

As short as she was and as thin as a stick as she was, Aunt Rena's voice carried all the power of a general as she answered.

"I know what you mean, and…" she peered over the top of her bifocals at the members of the family "…so do most of you. If you don't, it's high time you did."

She continued, "Your grandfather told me on his death bed that, as years went by, he would return to visit each member of the family. And …" she looked around the tables "…he continues to do just that, doesn't he, Lawrence?"

"Why don't you tell them of that time?" Ken's father asked of him. "You remember it, don't you?"

Ken remembered. Indeed, he remembered when his granddad had come to visit them after his death.

It seems Ken was about five or six when he and his dad were going hunting out near Scott's Point. His grandfather had died before Ken was born so he didn't know what he looked like. They were just past Newton Creek, walking along the Lake Michigan shoreline, when big cotton-like clouds filled the sky. The sky turned gray-black and large wind-swept clouds wrapped around them. A bright light started to glow. A man appeared from that light and walked up to his dad.

Ken said he thought it was an angel. The man put his hand on his dad's shoulder and told him that he was all right. He said that he was with his grandmother and not to worry about them anymore. Then he turned back into the light and, taking all of the clouds with him, he was gone in an instant. The darkness left the shoreline. Ken said his dad stood there for a moment staring at the lake. Before long he turned and started to walk back into the woods. They continued walking until the path turned into an old two-track where his dad stopped and told him that the man was Ken's grandfather.

"But granddad is dead, isn't he?" Ken remembered asking.

And his dad replied, "Yes, he's dead all right."

Ken said he always figured his dad to be the bravest man in the world. All kids think that about their dads, don't they? Nevertheless, he remembered his dad's arm was shaking hard as he reached out to put it across his shoulder as they continued walking back home.

Ken remembered that year's reunion and he remembered his Aunt Rena who had nodded her head up and down as he told his story. "That's the truth," she had said, "Once a year he returns to us. Now who has seen Granddad this year? Don't be afraid. Step up. We know you're not crazy. Tell us your tale."

According to Ken the last time we talked, this tradition continues every year at the family reunion.

Indian Burial Cemetery, St. Ignace

I discovered this story quite by accident. My husband and I were having dinner in a local restaurant in St. Ignace when I overheard a couple discussing their stay at the haunted campground at the top of the hill. Of course, I had to interrupt. In doing so, I discovered the following haunting tale.

The campground was filled for the weekend with fifth-wheels, tents, pop-ups, and elaborate motor homes parked among beautiful treed sites. Stories have been told and retold for many years about the ghosts at the campsites at the very back of the campground, the same area where an Indian burial site had been discovered in the '50's.

We need to go back in time to trace the beginning of this haunting. More than two centuries have elapsed since the Huron Indians populated the Straits of Mackinac. The Strait acted as a highway connecting two great regions. Mackinac Island was the "gathering place" for tribal chiefs and their tribes who had traversed the Great Lakes in long bark canoes since prehistoric times.

In St. Ignace, on a bluff that rises eighty feet above the level of the lake, there was a large communal grave that lay shrouded by overhanging limbs and thick undergrowth. Very little sunlight reaches into the area that, for over 300 years, masked the final resting place of fifty members of an ancient tribe, two dogs without paws, placed there to protect the spirits of those buried, and a long list of artifacts. Records indicate that the early Indians had a village at or near this burial site at the campground in 1670.

The communal grave may be taken as evidence of the Festival of the Dead. This was a custom among the Hurons and Algonquian Indians of the northern Great Lakes region to gather up, the remains of those who had died in the past ten years and rebury them in one central place. This was a great time of feasting, mourning and dancing. Nothing was more sacred to the Indians than their Festival of the Dead.

The mass grave was discovered in 1957 when a backhoe was removing gravel from the site. The owner, Mr. E. Richardson, removed some of the skeletons and found others entangled in roots some fifteen feet away, near the edge of the first site. A thorough dig of the pit area soon revealed a mass burial of the fifty-two human skeletons and two dog skeletons. Mr. Richardson displayed the bones in the mass grave to tourists and sold imitation artifacts in a small souvenir shop located near the front of the campground until 1970 when new owners of the Old Indian Burial Campground arrived.

It wasn't long before they began to hear weird tales from campers about the ghostly apparitions of Indians in the back of the campground near the burial site. One story began when a family with a little girl parked their fifth-wheel near the old burial site.

"Mom, can I play with the little boy outside?"

"Who is it?" Called her mother from the compact kitchen of their fifth-wheel.

"I don't know, but he wants me to play with him. He is dressed like an Indian boy."

The mother came to the doorway and saw a young Indian child, bare-chested and wearing a breechcloth. They both watched as the boy slowly melted into the summer sun. Needless to say, they were frightened and left to go back downstate that very day.

Another camper told the story of the time when she took an evening stroll back where the bones were then displayed. She heard footsteps on the path behind her. A storm had quickly brought thunder with the threat of rain to the campground and she started running back to her campsite. The footsteps followed her to her small trailer. She turned to look behind her to see an Indian wearing a breechcloth. He was standing under the pine trees near the edge of the path she had just followed.

"He was terribly sad," she said. "I felt his eyes pierce my soul and then he disappeared in a mist that was followed by heavy rain." The next day, she spread tobacco where he was standing and along the path to appease the spirits.

During this time the new owners decided to call the local tribal members to remove the skeletons. It was in June or July when the local tribal members came to investigate the site and soon after that, with help from the new owner, the bones were moved to the tribal center north of St. Ignace for an honorable burial. Since that time, spirits or trails of mist seem to slip through the tall pine trees at the now Tiki Campground.

About five years ago, an older Indian stayed at the campground near the front gate. He sold replicas of artifacts found in the mass grave. He said he could feel the Indian spirits near him and he that he had often seen the outline of an Indian walking through the grounds. The spirit would disappear like a mist in the wind as soon as he approached it.

I believe the spirits of this small handful of ancient Indian people remain in this place. The photograph I have included for this story is a picture of the exact spot of the massive burial site.

According to *An Early Historic Cemetery at St. Ignace* written by E. F. Greenman in the Michigan Archaeologist, Vol. 4, Number 2, July 1958, the following artifacts were found when excavating the site by gasoline shovel:

22 brass bangles

3 brass bells about 1/2-inch in diameter

3 brass coils about 5/8-inch in diameter

9 copper beads on a leather thong

1 tobacco pipe, stone, in effigy of an eagle or hawk, with part of the stem missing

1 small effigy of a human face, perforated in the ear-positions, and made of turtle shell

65 black spheroidal glass beads, opaque

31 small white spheroidal glass beads, opaque

3 white spheroidal glass beads, opaque

2 lumps of red ochre, about 3/8-inch in diameter

They were removed with care and brought to Ann Arbor to be photographed. Their location today is unknown.

For those of you who would like to visit the Tiki Campground, (formally the Indian Burial Campground) it is located north of St. Ignace at the corner of 200 S. Airport Road and State Street near the top of the bluff. When I last spoke to the owners, they informed me that the spirits of the site remain active. Things constantly disappear, especially in the office, and reappear in a different, unexpected place. Soft footsteps are often heard crossing the room to the door. I am afraid our spirits will have to pay a campsite fee if they wish to linger.

This is the site of the mass grave. There are nine spirits in this photo. How many can you find?

No Will-o'-the Wisp mislight thee;
Nor snake, or slow worm bite thee;
But on thy way
Nor making astray
Since ghost there's none to affright thee.

               ~ Robert Herrick (1591-1674)

The Haunted Cottage of Les Cheneaux Islands

The Les Cheneaux Islands hold many mysteries and stories of spirits are often told around the embers of the campfires of tourists and residents. This is one of them. It was told to me by two sisters who remember the cottage and this particular visit they made to their grandparents.

Sarah and Stacy's grandparents purchased the cottage in the mid-fifties. It sits near the edge of a jack pine forest on a small windswept bluff overlooking the cobalt blue waters of Lake Huron. The grandparents, Ray and Marlene, looked forward to long summer days of enjoying the area along with their children and grandchildren.

During their first year of ownership, late snowstorms, a rainy, cold spring, and a cool summer made the long drive from the city to the islands uninviting to most folks; however, Ray and Marlene came anyway. They were excited about their purchase and anxious to enjoy the peace and tranquility that island seclusion offered.

From the first days of residency, they felt a sense of unease surrounding the cottage. As the first weeks went by, Marlene told Ray she was bothered by a feeling of being on edge, of always looking over her shoulder, of feeling she was being watched. The feelings persisted even outside as she walked the path that led down to the shore.

"Now, honey, it's because we are so isolated here," Ray offered as they sat on the porch steps one evening in late July.

"Don't you feel it too? Haven't you ever felt as though someone is watching us, or caught a movement out of the corner of your eye? Not once, Ray?" she pleaded. "And," she hesitated, "how … well, how do you explain the strange globes of light that appear in so many of the pictures we have taken in and outside of the cottage?"

Ray stared out at the lake.

"You think I'm crazy, don't you, Ray?"

Ray put his arm around her shoulder and pulled her closer to him as he bent down and brushed her cheek with a light kiss. "I suppose I can think of times when I felt I was being watched, but I put it down to our being city folks and unused to the quiet here. You have to admit, honey, it is real dark up here and real quiet. Our imaginations can sure play tricks on us … if we let them. As for the lights in the film prints, I admit I was puzzled by them so I asked Mark at the camera shop. He said they're nothing but dust particles."

"Well, I'll be glad to leave here this week, Ray. I swear I am going to stay close to you and I refuse to look over my shoulder one more time!"

With that they gathered up their coffee mugs and retired for the night.

Sometime around two or three in the morning, Marlene was startled awake by the sound of muffled drums. She listened for a few moments to see if she could discover where the sounds were coming from.

"Ray?" "Ray?" she whispered into the darkness. "Ray." She

slowly slipped out of the bed and her voice rose as she turned on the lamp. "Ray! Where are you?"

Ray's voice came from outside, "I'm out here on the porch. Come here, but be quiet," he cautioned.

"What on earth are you doing out here?" she asked as she pushed open the screen door.

"Listen." He said.

"Drumbeats?"

"Yeah," he nodded, "but where are they coming from?"

They listened as a slow rhythm of drums echoed across the water.

"It must be the local tribe having a ceremony of some kind. The drums sound so very sad, don't they? Oh, look, isn't that summer heat lightning?" Marlene asked as she reached for Ray's hand.

"Not warm enough for heat lightning. We might get some rain before morning."

Ray's prediction proved true as the following morning's drive back to the city was cursed with thunderstorms and a hard rain all the way home.

Two weeks later found the pair working again at the cottage. Ray was painting the kitchen cupboards, while Marlene stood at the sink peeling potatoes for the evening's salad. The sky had darkened while they worked.

"Ray," Marlene said quietly. "Don't say a word but look at the screen door."

They both watched as the door opened slowly as if to let someone or something out. They stood in frozen silence as they both heard soft padded footsteps cross the porch and continue down the steps.

"What in hell was that?" asked Ray.

"That was the 'that' that has been watching us for weeks. That is the 'that' that has caused the frigid cold spots in the house. That is the 'that' that turns the lights on and off. That is the 'that' that scares the hell out of me, Ray, when I am alone."

"Probably the wind, Honey. The footsteps … well, more than likely it's the wind pushing the leaves across the porch. As for the wiring, it's all new. Power surges can cause that business."

"Ray, you are impossible sometimes."

"Gather your wits, Marlene. The grandkids are coming tonight and we don't want to scare them with all of this nonsense."

They continued working on various projects throughout the day. At one point, Ray seemingly misplaced his paintbrush.

"I swear, Marlene, I put it right there," he stated as he pointed to the counter top and the paint can.

They searched the entire kitchen but it had disappeared. Ray, finally admitting defeat, returned from the shed with a new brush and continued his work. As evening neared, they strolled down to the darkening lake as they waited for the kids: daughter Beth and her husband, Dave, and the two grandchildren Stacy and Sarah.

Dinner time came and went. No kids. As Marlene started to place dinner into the refrigerator she found the missing paintbrush, with the paint forming a puddle, on the bottom shelf. Her loud intake of breath brought Ray to her side.

"Explain this to me, Ray!" she cried as she held open the refrigerator door.

Ray's mouth gapped as he shook his head in disbelief.

"What the hell!" he exclaimed.

Neither of them said a word. What possible explanation could there be? Both of them became acutely aware of the drumming that followed the waves across the water. Tension built as they continued to wait. They anxiously peered into the darkness toward the road. The moon sent shadows slipping through the jack pines.

"They should have been here by now," said Marlene softly as she paced the length of the front room.

"Maybe they had car trouble," answered Ray. They worried throughout the night. Cell phones were an invention of the future.

Finally, Ray drove to the small grocery store about eight miles away to try to reach their overdue family. Marlene nervously waited at the cottage. As she sat in the living room trying to keep busy with knitting, she suddenly felt the air around her grow cold, then frigid. The hair on her neck stood up. She quickly got up and walked to the bedroom to get a sweater and returned to the living room. The fireplace crackled, bringing warmth to the room.

She had a problem with that. She did not light that fireplace and knew that Ray didn't light it. Or at least she thought she knew. She looked slowly around the room and again heard the drumbeats. The sound beat slowly, rhythmically. One was never sure if it was this sound of waves beating against the rocky shoreline to the east, or the echoes of a long ago Indian ceremony. Nervously, she hesitated by the fireplace, welcoming the warmth but frightened by it even being lit. *Perhaps, Ray started it,* she thought to herself. *I just didn't notice. It was sometimes hard to start. Maybe it took awhile to catch.*

She huddled in her sweater in the big leather chair by the door. She was chilled clean through. She watched the driveway through the window. The drumming kept time with her heartbeat. "Oh, God, where is Ray? Please let the kids be safe," she murmured.

She walked to the kitchen to pour some more coffee when the slamming of car doors brought her running to the porch. There were her kids and grandkids and Ray walking up the path.

"Where on earth have you all been?" she cried. "I have been so worried! Ray, where did you find them? I am so glad to see you!" she cried as she wrapped her arms around her grandchildren.

"Oh, Mom, we're fine," Beth called out across the yard.

"Well tell me what happened!" Marlene implored.

"Come on in and get something to eat first. Do you want coffee?" Ray asked, as he hauled sleeping bags up the steps. Stacy and Sarah, finally released from the confines of the car, ran in circles, happy to be free of "no's" and don't-do's.

"Coffee would be great," answered Dave.

"Me too," Beth joined in.

Once they were all seated, enjoying sandwiches and drinks, Beth told them about their experiences. "We were just up the road from here when a dead end sign practically blocked the road. Neither of us remembered it being there so Dave turned around and tried the south road. But he couldn't find it. We just kept going in circles. Then it started to rain. Hard. Thunder and lightning followed us back to Cedarville. We were tired from the long drive and decided to spend the night at the old hotel and that's where dad found us unpacking the car."

"It didn't rain here last night, kids," Ray said quietly as he looked at Marlene. "In fact, the moon lit up the yard like an electric light."

"Well it rained down the road and it really came down in buckets," replied Dave.

"And," said Beth, "we heard the Indian drums long before the thunder and lightning started. How can you stand that banging all night long up here, Mom?"

"You get used to them, don't you, Ray?"

"How do you explain the sign last night?" Dave asked.

"You two were just confused in all that rain and took a wrong turn. Now come on, enough talk; let's get all of you tucked into bed. We are going to have a great weekend!"

The cottage had three bedrooms with a narrow long closet between two of them–a very dark, long narrow closet. Across the hallway that ran the length of the cottage was a larger bedroom and a bathroom. Stacy and Sarah were excited to spend their first night up north. Grandma Marlene put them in the very last bedroom. It was a cozy room with soft warm blankets and feather pillows. Two small square windows, one over each bed, let the moonlight scatter patterns of jack pines waving in the wind across the room.

The girls snuggled down and were soon sound asleep. They both woke up to the sound of painful moans and weeping. It took them but a second to find their parents across the hall.

"Mom! Dad!" they shouted, as they ran to the bed.

"What on earth…?" cried Beth.

"Calm down you two," demanded their dad.

"There is something in our room!" the girls screamed together.

"It's moaning!"

"Ok girls, its okay. It's just the wind."

"I am not going back in there!" stated Stacy.

"Me either."

"Come on girls, let's have a look."

"No Dad! No! NO!"

The girls clung to their mother as Dave entered the small bedroom. A wall of frigid air pushed at him. He flipped on the light switch only to have it flicker and then go off. He abruptly stopped, took a step backwards and listened.

What was that? A groan? From the closet?

"God, it's cold in here." he muttered as he started back across the hall. He paused again, A shadow slipped down the hallway. What was that, Dave thought. "Ray? Marlene?" he whispered into the darkness. "Damn drums," he mumbled, "Don't they ever stop?" *There's nothing wrong,* he thought as he crossed back into their bedroom. *Those darn kids have even got me spooked.*

"Nothing there," he said out loud, as he climbed back into bed. "But you girls can stay with us tonight."

He didn't know the lights had come back on in the bedroom and the frigid air had left with the shadow that had slipped down the hall.

Morning arrived to the smell of hot coffee and cinnamon rolls. They gathered together on the front porch to watch an amazingly beautiful sunrise. Beth urged Dave to tell her parents about the episode of the girl's fright and the moans from the walls of the closet. After Dave retold the events of the previous evening, Ray told them of several of the mysterious happenings that had been occurring at the cottage.

"Have you ever cleaned out that hall closet?" Dave asked.

"I cleaned the front of it out," Marlene answered. "I just found a bunch of boxes filled with old newspapers and moth-eaten blankets."

"How far back does that closet go? And, Mom, why haven't you ever cleaned it out?" Beth wanted to know.

"I was always afraid to go all the way back, but I don't know why," Marlene offered.

"Well," Dave said, "let's go take a look. Ray, are there any lights back there?"

"Not that I know of. I'll get a couple of flashlights."

A sudden clap of thunder sent them all dashing into the kitchen.

They made a parade going down the hallway to the closet. Dave and Ray bent over and groped their way to the end wall. The flashlight beam spread over bare walls. "Nothing here," Ray called back to Dave.

Dave said, "I don't see anything either,"

"Wait a minute. Damn! Ouch!" Ray exclaimed.

"What's wrong, Ray? Did you find something?" Dave shouted.

"Yeah, there's a trap door here." said Ray. "Put the light over here, Dave, I'm going to pull the handle."

The trap door, crusted with dirt, fought being opened. Dust floated up and scattered away from the beam of the flashlight.

"What do you see, Ray?"

"It's a large bundle wrapped in … it looks like deer skin."

Ray managed to pull the bundle up from its resting-place. Dave's flashlight led them back through the long dark closet to the hallway where Beth, Marlene and the girls waited.

Ray carried the bundle to the kitchen table. Meanwhile, the thunderstorm had intensified. Lightning shattered the surrounding darkness as Ray removed the layers. They were in awe as they unwrapped the animal skins to reveal an Indian tunic made of two deer hides. Beneath it lay a shirt with heavily beaded panels and a pair of fringed leggings. They could not identify a square piece of leather that was filled with beads and what looked like bone tubes but they were amazed at the beautiful moccasins with beads running down the front and around the collar.

Ray now knew what they had found. He knew the clothing was Chippewa because of the moccasins. They were clearly identifiable with their center-seam and cuff. He knew that historically the Chippewa were called the "people of the puckered moccasin."

"We need to contact the members of the local tribe," he said as he held up a painted buckskin robe. "This find will be of great importance to them and we need to do it now."

"These things are beautiful," offered Beth.

"Not only beautiful but they are very old," answered her mother.

That same evening found the family seated with several tribal members. Silence filled the room as each garment was carefully revealed. Gasps of disbelief followed the removal of a pipe from its hiding place in the folds of the painted robe. The bowl was of red colored stone and the stem was ash. Clearly, the family had found an ancient artifact.

Arrangements were made to smudge the cottage. The Indian clothing and pipe were historically significant artifacts; it was important they be given a ceremonial burial in a sacred place as soon as possible. This was done according to the customs of the people. The troubled spirit of the cottage finally rested.

Throughout the years, many families have owned the cottage and delighted in the beauty of its location. Today, bathed in rays of sunlight that filter through the pines, the cottage seems to sleep as it waits for another new owner.

The Engineer, Sault St. Marie to Superior, Wisconsin

We continue our tour up to Sault St. Marie. I met this gentleman's daughter in a local café. She first told me the story, but I decided to meet with the man who had actually experienced this haunting trip across the peninsula many years before.

We sat in a red imitation leather booth in a small café located in downtown Sault St. Marie. He was an elderly man with pure white tufts of hair that stuck out from beneath an old fishing cap. He sat with his hands tightly folded in front of him as he told me the following story. He swore to its truth, as he had been one of the men that traveled on that last train run with the dead engineer.

"At that time," he began, "a group of us who had become friends had been with the Duluth South Shore and Atlantic Railroad for about fifteen years. The train ran from Sault St. Marie, Michigan to Superior, Wisconsin. Our buddy, Ed, the engineer, had died of a sudden heart attack while at the Sault on a stormy evening just prior to our return run to Wisconsin. We decided to bring Ed's body home on the train that night as a kind of salute to his years of service instead of shipping it home by the usual means. We brought Ed down to the local undertaker and he laid out Ed's body real neat in a wooden box. Because it was a freight train run, we put the box in the caboose and continued our preparations to leave the station."

The old man looked sadly out to the rain swept highway that ran along the shore of Lake Superior. He hesitated, as if he needed time to gather his thoughts, then slowly continued.

"We were all set to go. The new engineer who came into the cab of the engine was a quick replacement for Ed, and George, the fireman, saddened by the loss of his friend, kept his head down and went to work. Once they started on their way, the engineer kept encouraging George to go faster and faster, but the fireman knew you could only go so fast on this run. There were certain bridges you had to slow down on for safety's sake. However, this engineer, he broke all the rules: we made it to Wisconsin in almost half the time we should have. When we arrived, the air was heavy with humidity and fog. I watched the engineer get off the cab. I remember he slowly turned around and gave a short wave of his hand to us as he walked into the mist.

"George and the rest of us on the run that night walked back to the caboose and removed the wooden box that we had put Ed into. When we got it to the funeral home, we opened it to say a final farewell to our friend."

He paused "To this day I have a hard time telling this story and I sure don't tell it to everyone. To this day, it seems like it never happened. But it did ... we all know it did."

Again, he looked out at the rain. There was another long pause. Then he looked at me – as if daring me to believe what he was about to say.

"We were stunned as we looked down into the wooden box. Oh, yeah," he nodded his head, "it was Ed all right. However, Ed's face was filthy dirty with soot and he was wearing his chopper gloves, the same chopper gloves I put into a paper bag to give to his family. We all knew then that it was Ed that drove the train that night back home to Superior, Wisconsin. We all know it was impossible what we had witnessed, but that didn't change the fact that it had happened."

A Living Spirit, Sault St. Marie

It was raining that thick rain that turns to a slushy mess in seconds in this part of Michigan and makes driving more of a life-and-death sport than a mere challenge. In the past months, I had become known as an amateur ghost hunter in the Upper Peninsula, much to the chagrin of my poor husband. We receive calls on a weekly basis about he, she, or it appearing in odd places and at seemingly inconvenient times. On our last visit to the Sault after the interview with the old gentleman, a woman had approached me about the haunting of a house nearby. She reminded me of one of the local black jack dealers at the Native American casinos that have sprouted up all over Northern Michigan. Though I arranged to meet her, I really wasn't looking forward to another story about mysterious footsteps and floating candles.

I followed her directions to Little Italy, the oldest part of Sault St. Marie. In the early 20's, it had been a beautiful area of the small town; however, today, in the gray drizzle, dark windows in empty houses peered out at the narrow street. As I drove along the edge of the curb, I checked house numbers. I slowly pulled forward to an aged two-and-a-half story house with a wrap-around porch and wilting steps. On the porch was the woman sitting in a rocking chair. She looked different today. The long black hair flowing down her shoulders made her appear much younger than when we had met at the restaurant, although it was hard to tell for sure as I stared at her and the house through the sloppy rain. She beckoned to me as I left the car and approached the steps.

"Welcome," she said softly with haunting eyes. "Come in."

"Have you been waiting long?" I asked as I gingerly made my way up the steps.

"No," she replied, as she turned to open the door.

I noticed with envy the wide turquoise bracelets on her wrists. I shivered in the dampness and followed her down a long, dark hallway, wishing I had grabbed a cup of strong hot coffee before I came. She led me through a dining room filled with dead ferns and a large table surrounded by eight upholstered chairs. It smelled musty and old. I thought I caught a weak baby's cry coming from somewhere above us. She didn't appear to notice. We passed through another smaller, darker hallway that led into a mid-century kitchen. The aroma of coffee filled the room. She must have read my mind, I thought. She finally turned to me and held out her hand saying,

"I'm Stephanie. Please, let's sit here by the window." She indicated a small round table and two chairs that overlooked a backyard strangled with an overgrowth of shrubs and weedy grass. I noticed the slushy rain had turned to snow. Before I asked my first question, I knew the answer.

"Is this the house?"

"Yes," she murmured softly.

"Is it vacant now?"

"Yes," she answered as she nodded her head and looked toward the hallway. At least I think it's vacant."

I shivered again, but not from the cold or dampness.

"Let me tell you about this house. It has seen many things."

"Then you believe it is still haunted?" I questioned as she poured us coffee and sat down to stare out at the forlorn landscape. She answered in a hushed voice,

"Yes. Often troubled spirits return."

My nerves tingled as I took a sip of coffee. She continued in a hushed tone.

"A long time ago, two men moved into this house in the early spring." Her voice lowered to a whisper. The wind picked up outside. I could feel a draft spread up my back and across my feet. It seemed to be getting darker. I glanced at my watch. It was two o'clock in the afternoon. Was that a baby's cry again? The dark shadows in the old kitchen edged closer."

She hesitated, then began again,

"One night there was a powerful thunderstorm. One of the men was nearly frightened to death that night. He said he had seen a woman standing on the porch through the living room window. First he saw just her face, and then she slowly materialized through the curtain of rain with her arms outstretched to him. He went to the front door to ask her if she needed to come in but she wasn't there. He ran to the end of the porch and around to the back entry. She had disappeared.

"He was soaking wet when he returned to the living room. There, in the center of the room, was the woman. She once again held out her hands to him. He was about to ask how she got in when she slowly faded into nothingness. Fear gave him momentum as he ran from room to room in a frenzy, turning on lights and slamming doors behind him. He turned a corner into the first floor hallway and there she was again. He watched as she came toward him with her arms held out, teardrops of blood falling from her wrists. He ran down the hallway to his bedroom and locked the door. Silence. He strained to hear any sound.

"Suddenly the house was filled with weeping from every corner. Anguished sobs filled the rooms. Thunder cracked and rolled in the distance and the lightning seemed to follow him as he ran from the house and down the dirt road that led to the center of town.

"Shortly after that night, the two men came back to the house to remove their belongings. I met them on the front porch. They told me what had happened. Many times, they said, they had heard sobbing and the sound of someone pacing in the hall, or here in the kitchen, or on the stairway going to the second floor, only to discover there was nothing there. Once, one of them said, he thought he had seen a woman standing near the dining room table but he thought it might have been just a trick of the gathering twilight. The other admitted he had seen a woman wearing a dark shawl in here in the kitchen. A baby's crying often woke them up at night and both of them had frequently sensed being watched, especially here in the kitchen."

She continued to look out the window at the bleak landscape as she paused in her recital.

"In here?" I asked.

"Yes," she replied. I looked casually around the room and tried to peer into the dark corners. The dimming light caught the edge of a thick bracelet as she sipped her coffee.

She continued, "There were many times, they said, when they would catch a shadow out of the corner of their eye, a slight movement in the hallway, or on the stairs. There is a story told by the local people of an Indian girl who came to live here with the father of her baby. He left her here one night during a storm promising to return for her. He never did. This was a great shame to me; I mean her and her tribe. The tribe would cast her out. It is the custom. She knew this and could not face her people's shame. She killed her newborn baby and then killed herself, here in the kitchen, by slashing her wrists."

"In this kitchen?" I asked again.

"Yes. In this room. She was found here," she gestured, "on the floor, covered in her blood and the blood of her child."

"Right here where we are right now?"

"Yes. I believe her spirit is trying to leave here."

"You mean you believe she is still here?" I quickly responded, as I shivered from the cold draft that crept up my spine. She moved to the stove to prepare another pot of coffee. As she measured coffee from a tin, she continued.

"Because I smudged this house according to the teachings of my people. I am Ojibway. The four sacred medicines in our culture are tobacco, cedar, sweet grass, and sage. The medicine that I used in this house was white sage. It is known as medicine sage. After it is dried, you use it to smudge. Do you know what smudge is?"

I shook my head, "No."

"Smudging is taking a pinch or two of the sage and placing it in a smudge bowl. You must first remove all metal from your person to perform this ritual. Medicine sage is known for its cleansing properties. The smoke from the burning sage is powerful medicine. I smudged this house from room to room. I made sure to smudge all of the corners, and all the mirrors. As I did this, I hoped the spirit would cross over into the light. Many spirits do not realize they are dead," she repeated, "and that the home is no longer theirs. They don't … realize they're dead"

Her voice melted away. She hung her head. The hair on my neck and arms stood up when she slowly began again.

"She doesn't know she is dead. She remains here."

Again, she continued as if in a trance.

"As the sage smoked in the bowl, I used my hand to fan the smoke throughout each room. As I walked from room to room, I begged her spirit to leave this place. When I came here to the kitchen, I felt a great loss and sorrow. Sorrow so deep it sickened me. I felt myself falling, my heart cried out poor baby, poor, poor baby."

She walked over to the long counter by a darkened window next to the sink. She picked up a small bowl to show me. "This is my smudge bowl. I left it here that day. This is the first time since that day that I have been back in this house. The magic didn't work. She remains here."

She returned to the table where we had spent most of the afternoon. She leaned over to peer out of the window and whispered,

"Night seems to have stolen upon us. I feel like I am balancing on the edge of reality. What is real? Oh God, what is real?"

She turned and leaned toward me, "You'll spend the night, won't you?" she implored as she began to fade away. Her hand reached toward me.

"You'll spend the night won't you–won't you–won't you…?" Her voice echoed and drifted away.

I sat looking in amazement. I looked all around me. I expected to see her standing somewhere in the room. I slowly stood up.

"Stephanie," I whispered.

"Stephanie?"

I grabbed my camera, purse, and coat and ran from that house. Who had I interviewed? Who met me on the porch? Who was Stephanie? What had happened back there? I drove with a careless abandon to a nearby service station. I wrapped my shaking hand around a cup of hot coffee and started the long drive back across the peninsula to home.

To this day, I can't explain what had happened. I know, at least I think I know, Stephanie is the very same woman that invited me to investigate that house, but she must also be the spirit that haunts the house. She is the Indian girl who took her own life and that of her baby.

I know I leave the reader somewhat confused. I apologize. Nevertheless, you must understand, I cannot explain anything about this entire episode. I have since learned there are ghosts that do not know they are dead. They continue to try to complete their lives. I believe Stephanie is one of them.

Mr. and Mrs. Brown, Sault St. Marie

This story came to me from a gentleman who once lived in the Sault. He now lives in Marquette. The son of Mr. and Mrs. Brown told him the following story. Mrs. Brown was over 100 years old when she told this story and her son had retold it several times. He is also gone now.

There was a Mr. and Mrs. Brown who lived on the South Road back in the 1900's. Everyday Mr. Brown would take his wagon into town to see if he could find a day's work. Mrs. Brown would stay home to do the household chores; the wash, making bread and cutting wood. On this particular day, as Mrs. Brown went to a nearby stream to get water, a large black dog appeared out of nowhere.

The dog tried to grab the handle of the water bucket, she said, "as if he meant to help me carry it." As the day progressed, the big dog remained by her side, following her footsteps as she went about her work. When she started to carry wood from the woodshed to the house, the dog picked up pieces of wood and carried them to the porch, dropped them and returned for another load.

When she finished, she gave him a friendly rub on his ears, some water, and scraps of food. He lay by her side as she sat on the porch in the late afternoon sun waiting for Mr. Brown to return home. The dog was good company and she found herself petting him and talking to him. She hoped Mr. Brown would let her keep him. Mr. Brown arrived shortly before the sky started to darken. Rumbles of thunder could be heard in the distance. As he greeted his wife, a wagon with two men and a woman appeared around the curve of the dirt road. The black dog stood up and moved closer to Mrs. Brown. As the wagon pulled into the yard, one of the men asked if they could stay the night in a tent on the property. Mr. Brown could think of no reason to refuse.

During dinner, Mrs. Brown's face lit up with a smile, as she explained to her husband the dog's mysterious appearance and behavior that day. She asked him if she could please keep the big dog, saying how safe she felt with him by her side. Mr. Brown did not often refuse his wife's requests and said of course, they would keep him.

When they retired for the night, the dog lay in the hallway guarding the bedroom door.

Around two a.m., the storm that had been threatening the evening broke. A hard, cold rain swept across the porch and pounded the roof. Mr. Brown, feeling bad for the travelers, walked down and invited the folks in from their tent. The dog went with him. When they returned, the dog ran up the stairs to the hallway and again sat in front of the bedroom door.

"He should have been soaking wet, but his fur," said Mrs. Brown, "was as if it had just been brushed. It shined in the oil-lamp light." The travelers made their bed in the kitchen. Night crept on. All was silent.

Suddenly shrill barking and deep throaty growls startled the Browns from their sleep. The dog was attacking a man with a knife in his hand in the hallway. Mr. Brown grabbed his shotgun and fired it into the air. The man flew down the stairs and out the door. His two companions followed him into the night. The dog stood with the Browns as they watched the wagon leave the property. The dog remained on the porch.

The following morning, the Browns called for the dog. They called and called. They set out food and water for three days in hopes that he would return. They knew that dog had saved their lives. Sadly, they never saw him again.

About two weeks after that, frightening night, Mr. Brown returned home carrying in his arms a small pitch-black puppy with the biggest paws you have ever seen. Mrs. Brown kissed her husband fondly on the cheek as she marveled how beautiful her puppy was.

Later that year, they heard of a man being robbed and killed in Engadine by two men traveling with a woman. From all reports, the killers were never caught.

Whitefish Point Mystery

This story comes to me from a couple that vacationed in the Upper Peninsula during the summer of 2004. They were especially interested in visiting Michigan lighthouses. Seul Choix Point Lighthouse and the ghost of Captain Joseph W. Townshend intrigued them, but later, they encountered another strange occurrence in Whitefish Point near Paradise, Michigan. I am going to let the author tell her story in her own words.

"I will try to tell you what happened as best as I can as some of the feelings that we experienced are hard to put into words. We went to Whitefish Point because I wanted to take pictures of an active light at night. We arrived there about 8 p.m. in early August. A few people were on the beach collecting rocks. Dan and I wandered about looking for driftwood, rocks, and just admiring at the lake. The others left as twilight began to spread over the lake.

"I walked down to the edge of the lake and saw some rocks in the water that I wanted. The weather had turned gloomy and damp as if it were going to rain. The wind had picked up and I shivered as I leaned toward the water's edge. Every time I went to pick up a rock, the water would come up and try to get me wet–first up to my hand and then up to my feet: playing tag with a lake was a new experience! Dan soon joined me and was looking at the shoreline through a video camera that has night vision. He wandered up the beach and I continued my quest for the best stones. I remember looking over my shoulder at the lighthouse and wondering why the light still wasn't on.

"It was after 9 p.m. and certainly dark enough. Strangely enough, I could see it revolving and thought it must be burnt out. I reached out to grab another stone when suddenly I got a very cold chill down my spine and the hair on the back of my neck stood up. Something urged me to look out into the lake to the northwest. I saw nothing but black water and a darkening sky. I kept watching but I felt like I was being pulled into the dark water. It made me nervous and afraid so I ran up to the beach away from the water's edge.

"An eerie, mournful feeling hung over me. I felt tears on my face and started running to Dan. He was standing looking out to the same place I had been. When I asked him what he saw, he said he just wanted to get back to the truck. I told him I had a real strange feeling and he replied that he did too. He said he just wanted to leave. As we approached the truck, the feelings of urgency lessened. I thought I heard someone walking behind us in the sand, but when I looked, no one was there. I don't know how Dan got ahead of me. I slowed down because of all the rocks I was carrying in my pockets. Again, I heard someone behind me. This time I felt a presence. I turned quickly, but nothing was there or if there was, I was seeing right through them. We sat in the truck in silence. The lighthouse light still wasn't on and it was going on 10 p.m. We drove back to our motel. Neither of us said a lot.

"The next day we went back to take a tour. It had stormed during the night and the morning brought fog. After touring the buildings, we again walked down to the beach. We heard a fog horn in the distance. We thought there might be a freighter on the lake. There were almost 35 people on the beach, walking and collecting rocks. Dan was recording the fog-shrouded shoreline.

I stood peering into the mist when suddenly I saw a ship coming straight at us. Dan shouted he thought it would run aground. However, no one else appeared to see it. No one commented on how close it was or how dangerous. It continued to come at us and was only a half mile away when it entered a fog bank and completely disappeared.

"There was a woman standing next to me taking pictures and she never said a word about the ship that was so close to shore. All the ship left behind was a fog signal that sounded several times until there was only silence. Dan thought he had film of the ship, but when we tried to review it, there was nothing on the tape except fog. The one thing we remembered seeing was the stack. We were puzzled when we discovered the stack was from an early Canadian line that was no longer in service on the lakes. We checked the following day at Sault St. Marie to see if any ships matching our description went through the locks that day. All we got was some strange looks and were told only one ship had come through the locks the previous day and it was upbound into Lake Superior.

"So I ask, was it a ghost ship? What ship was it? Why did only Dan and I see it that day?"

I have heard from several people who have claimed to have seen ghost ships in Whitefish Bay.

"I met a man walking up the stairs who wasn't there.
He wasn't there again today; I wish he'd stay away."
(Author Unknown)

The Doctor, Newberry

This particular story interested me because it reminds me so much of my own father who "stopped by" the hospital to see me after the birth of my third child. Dad had passed away on January 19 of that year, but he saw his newest granddaughter in the spring on April 23 of that same year.

This story came to me from the doctor's daughter.

It was a great day to be hunting grouse. The bright sunlight filtered through leaves turned golden by cold nights and warm October days. The doctor was an avid hunter, but for months he had been terribly upset about the possible closing of the state hospital. Hunting was a way to relax–that and smoking three packs of Lucky Strikes a day. The doctor walked slowly that fall morning. His forehead beaded with perspiration. His heart beat hard against his chest. Suddenly, he fell forward. His dog stayed next to him.

The day quickly waned into twilight, as it does in October. Because Doc was a punctual man, his wife kept dinner waiting for him. By the time the sun had set, the state troopers were at her door. Doc had been found dead of a heart attack.

Later that winter, several unusual incidents began. The first was the dog. He would become excited for no apparent reason. It was as if he were playing ball with someone in the living room. His tail would thump on the floor as he sat in expectation of the toss. He would jump up then dash down the hall to the bedroom and back again. He would twirl and dance in the living room and when he finally settled down, he would fall asleep by Doc's chair in the living room.

Meanwhile, partridge feathers began to appear in strange places, for instance, in dresser drawers, magazine pages, pages of books, under rugs, on windowsills and in soapy dishwater. Such strange occurrences still happen today.

One night, the family returned home to find the lights on in the doctor's study or "hunting" room. They were somewhat frightened because no one had been in there since the doctor had died. The light could not be turned off that night–they couldn't find the key to the door. Shortly after that, in the middle of the night, Doc's wife woke her oldest son and asked him to come into the living room with her. When he walked in, he discovered both the TV and the light by his father's chair were on. His mother explained it was the third time that night she had returned to the room to turn everything off.

It wasn't until Doc's wife discovered that "their" song was playing whenever she turned on the local radio station–either at home or in the car that she finally understood. She had been thinking of suicide after the loss of her husband. Now she knew he was trying to tell her that he was still with her and needed her to take care of their family.

She went into the living room and turned off the TV again. She sat in his chair and said, "Joe, please stop. I understand. I really do understand." She turned off the lamp beside his chair and returned to bed.

Since that time the strange happenings have stopped, although there still remains an occasional partridge feather to be accounted for.

Guess Who Woke Up The Dead?
Munising

Upon leaving Newberry, our road tour takes us across M-28 and the famous Seney Stretch. This slice of road in the Upper Peninsula was once voted the most boring piece of highway in Michigan. You do need to keep your eyes open for deer along this highway and, if you are traveling at night, be aware of the many reports of UFOs that have dotted the media through the years. Munising is our destination. This area abounds with ancient legends of the Pictured Rocks, Indian myths and the spirits of the dead.

Much like the legends of Indian spirits that haunt the ancient cemetery on Grand Island and the Pictured Rocks trails, stories of hauntings slip through conversations in the early morning coffee clutches of this sleepy tourist town.

"Footsteps shuffled up the basement steps. The basement door opened … seconds passed … then it closed with a soft click. Mary froze at the snack bar where she had been making peanut butter cookies. She slowly turned around to face the intruder. No one was there … just a thickening of ice cold air. This wasn't the first time this had happened to her in this house."

Surrounded by huge jack pines and a tall cedar hedge, the house sits square on its stone foundation on a corner lot near downtown Munising.

The Dickersons' were from downstate Grand Rapids. They purchased the house from an estate in the early 70's. Both were excited about moving to the Upper Peninsula. They were retired and looked forward to remodeling the old house. John's hobby was carpentry and Mary loved to decorate. They had moved walls, changed hallways, moved doorways, and completely changed the traffic pattern of the entire downstairs. Shortly after they began the makeover, they started to notice several small strange incidents. Indeed, today was not the first time Mary had heard those footsteps. They usually followed the same pattern. They shuffled up the basement steps, the door opened and closed. They then came around the corner of the kitchen and into the dining room. They stopped there for a moment, then continued into the hall. They went slowly upstairs to the bedrooms and disappeared. These footsteps were only a small sample of the incidents that occurred during their stay in the old green house.

Mary was making the bed in the master bedroom one day when she heard what sounded like whispers from the corner near the new closet. She carefully pulled aside the clothing but nothing was there. There was nothing to make a whispering-like sound. This happened so many times that one day Mary whispered back. The first time she did this, the other whispering stopped." There," thought Mary, "That will show you." However, the next time she tried, it the whispers grew louder and louder until she left the room in dismay.

One bright afternoon, Mary ran into the bedroom to grab a sweater from the closet. In the corner of the room, she glimpsed a short elderly lady with a prayer book in her hands. She had a shawl over her shoulders and a strange bonnet on her head. You have to know Mary to understand what she did next.

"Oh," she said, "excuse me, I just need my sweater." Mary suddenly realizing what she just saw, turned around in time to catch the startled look on the old woman's face and then watched her slowly fade into the wall.

John never mentioned anything was wrong until their first winter in the house. You have to live in Munising to understand snow. It snowed and snowed some more. Snow piled up over the mailboxes and blanketed the hills that surround the bay. John shoveled snow off the back porch and driveway daily. He never shoveled the front porch or the basement entry.

One night as they were sitting in front of the old fireplace, they heard the sound of a shovel scraping on the front porch. John got up to see who was helping out. He looked through the dinning room window to see snow flying through the air. He ran to the front door and pulled it open,

"Mary! Mary!" he shouted. "Come here!" They stood in the open doorway and looked in amazement at the newly shoveled porch and steps. Although the porch was clean, the sidewalk was left undone and there was not a footprint anywhere around the area. They looked at each other and ran to the back door porch that overlooked the basement entry. Sure enough, the path to the basement had been shoveled clean, too. The next morning they found an old pair of gloves hanging on the fence post next to the back gate. But other than that, they never discovered who had helped shovel the snow.

When the kids, now in their late '30's, came home for the holidays, they told stories of waking up to find an old woman tucking the blankets in around their chins. They thought they were dreaming until one of the daughters told her brother about this realistic dream. He, in turn, told her about the smell of lilies of the valley in the mornings and not being able to keep his bedroom door closed, even after stuffing a sock in it and pulling it closed.

They compared notes and said they often saw dark shadows in

the long hallway that seemed to slip into the walls if you looked too closely. And heard footsteps that came up to the edge of the bed and then left; of someone sitting on the edge of the bed and feeling the bed actually sink down before having enough courage to kick your feet and roll over.

The Dickersons left the house in 1998. When contacted as to why they left, Mary said the house didn't want them anymore. She wouldn't explain further. The realtor who sold the house told me the new owners had tried to sue the previous owners for selling them a haunted house. But as everyone knows, that's a bunch of nonsense.

Brown's Addition, Munising

The lady who told me this story was a friend of my father's family. Although she was quite elderly at the time, her memories remained sharp. There was sadness in her voice the day that I visited. She has since passed away. She was a lovely old thing. These are her words you will be reading.

"Before my grandfather's death, I used to sleep upstairs in the big front bedroom of my grandmother's house in Brown's Addition. The windows there looked out over Munising Bay where I used to sit and watch for Grandfather to come up the hill from the fishing docks. This was back in the early '40's when the lakes were still full of good fish that were not contaminated with mercury or iron pellets. I still remember the smell of the warm July sun on the wooden docks and the sound of the fish tugs' motors as they crossed Sand Point channel heading for home.

"Granddad, my dad, and uncles would clean the fish, throwing the guts in the water for the seagulls to fight over. The fish were then put into wooden boxes that were filled with chipped ice. These were kept in the fish house. The fish house was filled with huge blocks of ice and sawdust and it acted like a freezer until the trucks came to deliver the fish to the cities.

"As I was saying, before my grandfather's death, I used to sleep in the big front bedroom in a narrow bed that was pushed next to a small window. Everyone–aunts, uncles, cousins, and visitors, had to pass my bed to climb into one of the other beds that lined the room. That's the way it was in those days. When Grandfather passed by me on his way to bed, he always leaned over and tucked my blankets in around my chin. I can still see his hands so wrinkled and worn from the cold winds and waters of Lake Superior.

"I didn't know what a spirit was back then. No one ever talked about ghosts or apparitions, at least not in front of me. Grandmother came from Germany and Granddad from Norway so with that background you would think that some of the superstitions from the old country would have been the subjects of those long winter conversations held around the wood stove in the kitchen, but I never heard a word. In spite of this, I knew there was something mysterious in that big old house, but I didn't think it was a ghost–at least not at that time. That didn't come until I was older.

"My Uncle Mike was a lieutenant in the Navy. He was killed in World War 1. After his death, I would hear music being played on the player piano that sat downstairs in front of the living room windows. My grandmother and Uncle Mike had both loved to play the piano. After Uncle Mike's death, she kept it polished until it seemed to produce an ethereal light of its own; however, to my knowledge, she never played it again. I was never allowed to even sit on its bench. I often heard its soft notes at the most unusual times during those years after his death. I would mention it to anyone who would listen and was told that the piano didn't work anymore. One time I remember grandmother looking down the hallway to where the piano sat in the living room, and then back at me, saying that it was my imagination.

"It was during this time, after my grandfather had tucked me in and I had snuggled down to sleep, that I would see Uncle Mike in his Navy uniform walk by my bed.

"I told grandmother that Uncle Mike was home again. I would

explain that I saw him walk past my bed! That, I was told, in a very strict voice, was my imagination.

"After Grandfather's death, I was moved to the small back bedroom, which only had one bed. The staircase came up from the living room into this room. It was here that Granddad's spirit returned to tuck me in at night. I can still see his hands as they pulled the blankets around my chin. I knew it was my granddad. When I told Grandmother, she just smiled and told me that he probably missed me. Through the years, it was also in this room that Uncle Mike's spirit continued to walk by the end of my bed as he made his way to the front bedroom. He always turned his head and smiled as he passed. I didn't know enough then to be frightened.

"Through the years, the fishing in the Great Lakes was severely damaged by the lamprey eel. Our fishing tugs were sold and the docks fell into disrepair. My father, along with some of my uncles, left the area in search of more dependable employment. Life wasn't easy for anyone during those years.

"After my parent settled downstate, I returned to visit Grandmother during the summer of my senior year in high school. I remember wondering if Granddad would still be there to tuck me in. I climbed the stairs my first night back with more than a little fear of what I would encounter. Perhaps, I thought, it had been my imagination as Grandmother suggested all those years ago.

"It wasn't. I had no sooner pulled the covers over my shoulders than I felt the tugging of the blankets around my chin. His dear hands were worn and cold, but I knew he was still taking care of me. The moon moved across the lake through my window as I listened carefully, and sure enough soft footfalls soon came up the stairs and walked to the end of my bed. I slowly opened my eyes just a little to see Uncle Mike as he turned and smiled at me just as he always had. He disappeared through the door to the big bedroom. I didn't tell Grandmother. I didn't tell anyone.

"That summer I took long walks down to the shoreline where the docks used to stand in the sunshine. They were gone now, leaving only skeletal remains of timbers bleached silver by the sun and water. I sat on the bluff overlooking the bay, hearing the fish tug's engine crossing the water. Was it a fishing tug coming through the channel of Sand Point? Was it my memories? "Grandmother died that winter. The house was sold.

During the times I have since returned there. My heart saddens for all that I lost in that wonderful place."

Ghosts of memories past but not forgotten. Are ghosts memories of people and places hidden in our subconscious? Is this what ghosts are? Memories?

The Spirits of Grand Island, Munising Bay

Grand Island is known to the Ojibwa as Kitchi Miniss, "Great Island" and, indeed, it is a great island parked in front and just to the west of Munising Bay. The island is eight miles long and home to Murray's Bay to the south and Trout Bay to the northeast. It is the largest island on Lake Superior's southern shore and the early home of the native Ojibwa and the ancient tribes before them.

I have watched storms come from out of nowhere and wrap the island in rain, sleet, snow, and ice. I have picked blueberries near Murray Bay and hunted for partridge on the two-tracks that snake through the woods and meadows of the island. I have fished Echo Lake for pike and walked to the north rim cliffs that rise 300 feet up from Superior's ice-blue water. I have also fought black flies the size of chipmunks.

The Cleveland Cliffs Iron Company logged the island for years, since the 30's, but you would never know it; they select-cut trees and the island flourished under their care. I saw a wolf while bird hunting there one fall. It stood right in the middle of the two-track I was walking and watched me as I approached. It's hard to imagine something that big and beautiful melting into the woods in a second's time. At one time, there were so many perch in Murray Bay, you could drop a worm and catch three at a time through the holds of the shipwreck, "Dreadnought." Such was the Grand Island that I knew as a child and in my early adult years.

My memories also include the caretaker of the island. He

had a house that sat on the edge of the woods near the landing.
There were several storage sheds where he kept an assortment of
mechanical stuff, various sizes of rope, and an old pick-up truck.
He told me stories of the ghosts that haunt the island. He knew
all of them, from the spirits of the early Indians to the haunting
of the island by the ghost of John Murray, one of the island's
earliest settlers.

Murray Bay is named for John Murray. He was an Irishman
who fell in love with his cousin's fiancee. The two men fought a
duel over the lass that resulted in the cousin's death and Murray
fleeing to America. He migrated west, eventually reaching Grand
Island where he built a small house on the point of today's Murray
Bay. He is said to have taught the children of Abraham Williams
and later his grandchildren, but then he turned to drinking and
became a hermit. (Alger County: A Centennial History, 1985)

There are many stories of his death. Most common is the story of
one of the Williams' kin discovering him hanging from a gnarled
white pine at the eastern end of the bay, his body swaying in the
north wind while sea gulls cried above him. Another tells of him
throwing himself off the northern cliffs of the island and his body
washing up on the sand beach of Trout Bay. Regardless of how he
died, his is one of the spirits that haunt the island.

Although I have heard some scary stories about Grand Island,
I never gave them much credence because I had spent so much
time on the island and never found anything unusual; that is,
the feeling of being watched isn't really unusual, is it? It wasn't
until after the National Park Service took over care of the island
that tourists, virtually unknown on the island until then, began
sharing tales of the strange occurrences they experienced while
visiting the island. Therefore, listen closely to the following story
told to me by two tourists from Wisconsin that wish to remain
anonymous.

"After hearing of the island from the storyteller, Larry Massie, who refers to Grand Island as one of Michigan's insular jewels, we knew we had to visit it and see for ourselves the beauty of which he spoke. He had told us about the exploits of the ancient Grand Island hornet rite where 'Naked young braves would arm themselves with a short stick and sally forth to attack a hornet's nest. Whoever stood his ground the longest while being repeatedly stung by the angry insects was judged the bravest.' He also related the tale of why the Indians didn't want the missionaries to camp on their island anymore. It seems one of the sandy points on the southern tip of the island had sunk due to missionaries prayers which had driven the Great Spirit out from under the point. The Indians were afraid if the missionaries remained, the entire island would sink.

"A hot, muggy day in late July found us crossing the water to Williams Landing. My wife and I had decided to camp on the edge of Murray Bay for a few days and we were anxious to get started before dark. Nothing notable happened that first night, but the following morning, we were taken by surprise by the appearance of a man dressed somewhat strangely in what looked to be dirty deer hides. He was carrying an old musket in one hand and a bundle in the other. He walked past our campsite and headed for the path to the thumb of the island. He looked right through us and as he passed, a wall of frigid air passed with him. Quite frankly, he scared the living hell out of both of us. My wife looked at me and asked who on earth was that. I didn't have a clue.

"We continued our morning chores while deciding to hike up to the northern part of the island. It would be a hot day so we dressed in shorts, cotton tops, hiking boots and brought along backpacks that would carry our lunch. It was a beautiful day, blue sky and sunshine. We didn't encounter any other visitors on our way up the twisting path.

"Around noon, we climbed a small cliff and unpacked sandwiches and water bottles. We sat on a broken log overlooking a field of flowers filled with Indian paintbrushes and Queen Ann's lace. Then we noticed the quiet. Not a sound wrinkled the air. The meadow seemed to hold its breath. Then, we watched as two Indians, fully dressed in the regalia of their ancient tribe, appeared on the edge of the field. The same strange man that passed our camp that morning joined them. They squatted while gesturing with their arms toward us. The Indians stood up and walked toward us as the man watched. They came within a yard of us when they simply faded away into nothing – like fog. I stepped back, holding my wife close to me.

"Suddenly the man was right in front of us. He looked into my eyes and, it seemed, into my soul. The air around us turned ice cold. Sweat beaded my forehead. "Go," he warned in a toneless voice as he pointed to the mainland. "Go, leave this place to those it belongs to." He melted into the air before I could catch my breath.

"My wife was clinging to me. It was then I noticed it was raining. It was coming down in sheets. We remained there watching the meadow as it slowly evaporated into nothing. The log was gone. The small cliff was gone. There was no meadow. We stood surrounded by jack pines, and birch trees. We were soaked through and shivering with cold as we made our way back to our camp. Apparently, time had stood still on the island. I know we had left our camp that morning around 8:30. I remember checking my watch just before we found the old log and that was about noon. Yet, when we returned to our campsite to pack up and leave it was only 11:30 in the morning.

"To this day I don't know what happened to us. We couldn't get off that island fast enough. The park ranger asked why we were cutting our stay short, because we had signed up for a campsite for three nights. I told him about the old man and the Indians and he just laughed as he said, 'So you ran into the ghost of John Murray, did you? You're not the only ones. The last few years some of our tourists have told us stories of encounters with the old man. We don't think anything of it. You folks just are not used to the isolation and quiet of the U.P. You let your imaginations get the best of you. Come back again some time. Next time you'll be more prepared for the solitude,' he called to us as we packed up our SUV and drove up the slight incline to M-28.

"Grand Island. We'll never go back. We don't care who the old man was or what happened up there in the woods. I don't care who believes us. That island can sink tomorrow, and I won't care. By the way, we later found out that it didn't rain that day, anywhere in the U.P. and yet we had a bag filled with soaking wet clothes in the back end of the SUV."

Again we have evidence that spirits do not like variation. Readers, please note the many stories of hauntings that occur after a change in the spirits' surroundings. Apparently, the spirits of Grand Island are not fond of the DNR's alterations to the island.

Grand Island located in Munising Bay.

The Ghostly Bells, AuTrain

Following M-28 to west of Munising, AuTrain lies in a cup of land surrounded by sand. It is a beautiful area to stop for a swim in the warm spring-fed waters of the river that flow into the icy-cold waters of Lake Superior. This story came to me from two people who were on a scavenger hunt. Although the story they told is short, it is quite unusual. They have requested that I not give their names or the location of the cemetery described.

Hazy autumn sunshine gilded the tombstones in the chill damp evening air. There was no wind yet the sound of wind chimes hung in the twilight. Kathy and John slipped through the rows of tombstones that lined the weed-grown lane. They were looking for the last item listed in a scavenger hunt for a Halloween party that evening. Kathy noticed that nearly all the tombstones she looked at recorded the deaths of elderly women in their '80's or '90's. Most of the deaths had occurred in the late 1800's.

"Over here, Kathy," whispered John. "I think I've found it."

"Let's see," Kathy said as she checked the paper against the writing on the tombstone in front of John. "Yes, this is it."

The stone read, "Once a thief, twice a thief. Someone has stolen my soul."

"I wonder what it means," said John as he picked up the last of the scavenger hunt's markers that was sitting on top of the tombstone.

A slight breeze chased fallen leaves across their path as they started walking back to the car.

"It's getting cold, John, and the sun's becoming a memory." Kathy laughed to shake off a sudden chill.

"I don't think it's cold," answered John, "but it is getting spooky out here. Let's head back." He waited for Kathy to get in the car. "Hurry up," he called. He looked behind him. Where was she anyway?

"Kathy!" he called. "Kathy!" He shouted louder. "Kathy!" Maybe she had gone into the woods to pee, he thought. He waited another fifteen minutes. He called for her several more times and still there was no reply, just the slight tinkle of wind chimes. Finally John climbed into the car and grabbed his cell phone. Just as he was dialing, Kathy knocked on the window of the passenger side of the car.

"John! Let me in!" she cried. She was still shouting at him as she climbed into the seat. "Where have you been?" she cried. "I have been calling and calling for you! I've looked all over for you. Where did you go?"

"Where have YOU been!" shouted John. "I have been waiting here and calling for you for a half an hour!"

"But I've been right here," said Kathy, "calling and calling for you."

"So have I." John replied strongly.

They both looked at each other.

Tendrils of what looked like fog crept up the surrounding jack pines as John backed the pick-up into a tight U-turn. A thin film of rain began to gather on the windshield.

"Holy Jeez!" John cried. "Look!"

In the dimming light, the ghostly shapes of old women slipped out of the pines through the mist into the cemetery. Dark hoods covered their bent heads; their shoulders hunched as they glided through the tombstones. They had small bells tied to their waists. Small bells that sounded like wind chimes as they walked. Then, like a whisper, they were gone. Nothing but the fading sound of wind chimes followed their ghostly path.

Ghostly Cemetery Bells

Hang a small wind chime in a doorway and a ghost, in passing, will make it sing.

The Mystery of North Lake Mansion, Ishpeming

Our road tour continues on through Marquette where there are stories of the Forest-Roberts Theater at NMU campus being haunted and other assorted hauntings in and about the city. We pass these tales that are readily available on the Internet, to interview a woman in Ishpeming who has had first-hand experience with a spirit. But first let me give you some background about this haunting.

On Wednesday, November 3, 1926, immigrant workers from Canada, Europe and Scandinavia who lived in the surrounding communities of Ishpeming, Diorite & North Lake reported to work at the Barnes-Hecker Mine. The mine is the property of Cleveland-Cliffs Iron Company. It… "was first explored in 1907 and developed in a swampy area in 1917. Underground dams were in place as safety precautions, and the draining of nearby North Lake and the overlying swamp in the early 1920's kept the mine a mostly dry working environment."

According to *No Tears in Heaven*, written by Thomas Friggins, the Cleveland Cliffs Iron Company maintained a diligent safety effort that included monthly and weekly inspections. Monthly, nine safety inspectors investigated all aspects of the mine operations. The Barnes-Hecker was last inspected three weeks prior to the disaster. But mining is a dangerous occupation, no matter what safety precautions have been taken and the 50 men who entered the Barnes-Hecker that cold November day had no idea that tons of mud, water, rocks, and debris would pour into the mine from above at 11:20 that morning, leaving forty-two widows and one-hundred-thirty-two minor children without a father by that evening. Michigan's greatest mining disaster ended with one survivor, who was haunted by nightmares the rest of his life.

Mining Superintendent Charles Stakel did not conduct his scheduled weekly inspection that day. Instead, he was at the Morris-Lloyd Mine when he got word of the emergency. It is believed that the mansion he lived in is haunted by his restless spirit, guilty over the disaster.

Old houses, theaters, buildings, and castles are haunted because of the things that have happened there. It is as if the atmosphere of the location creates a vortex of emotions. The electric energy left from a human life seems to linger until the energy is spent. This may take years or a matter of days. I believe this is what has happened at the North Lake mansion.

The mansion has four floors filled with twenty-two rooms. Extensive grounds at that time contained a stable and garages and there is some evidence of a summerhouse. Once owned by the Cleveland Cliffs Iron Company, the home was intended for the use of mining personnel. It was years after the disaster and the death of Charles Stakel that whispers started about the large house.

The following story is from one of the daughters of a family that once owned the old mansion.

They first noticed the erratic behavior of the electric lights. New wiring had been completed at great expense prior to their purchase but in spite of this improvement, the lights would turn on and off at will. The family would make quite certain the lights were off in all twenty-two rooms before leaving the house for any amount of time. On their return, all four floors would often be lit up like a Christmas tree, or all the lights only in the maids' quarters would be on. Sometimes just one light would appear to move across the top floor as if being carried by some unknown force. Although off when they left, the light at the front entrance would often burn brightly to welcome them home again. Many times the family would enter the house and rush to the rooms where the lights were seen shinning brightly only to find darkness when they arrived.

What scared the daughter the most was when she climbed into bed to read herself to sleep. Just as her eyes got heavy, her lamp would turn off. She remembers lying there staring into the darkness, her hands clutching the bedcovers to her chin. In time, she said, she got used to someone turning off her lights for her. She remembers her father complaining about the poor job the electricians did with rewiring, but nothing they did ever improved the erratic behavior of the electricity.

Cold drafts would wrap themselves around an object, or seem to follow them from one room to another. Always icy-cold air permeated the surrounding area where things had occurred. There were frequently cold spots especially in the basement near the old furnace and upstairs in the large bookcase-filled library. Frigid spots would welcome anyone that approached the long hallways that ran the length of the old house in the early morning hours. The parents' bedroom was susceptible to cold spots by the windows overlooking the front driveway.

The cold scared the family, as it seemed it to precede sighting an apparition. First appearing as a thick mist, the apparition would gleam faintly. It was a tall man, wearing a dark brown suit with a belt around the waist and tall brown boots that came up to his knees. He always appeared in the evenings and especially in the month of November. Rain also seemed to make him more active. He never hurt anyone, but his presence scared them to death when they were younger.

The first time he was noticed was after a heavy snowfall near Thanksgiving. There he was, sitting in a chair by the dining room table. He looked like a real person but disappeared when her father entered the room. Her mother was so frightened she nearly passed out. Of course they had to eat by candlelight that night as the electricity was out again, but only the dining room was in darkness. The chandelier crystals clinked against each as the family felt the air move around them and the ice-cold mist faded again. The children were told it was a trick of the light and continued with their turkey dinner.

Their father was away on business the next time the apparition made himself known on another snowy night a few weeks later. They were sleeping when a terrible pounding slammed the four exterior doors. The deafening noise vibrated against the walls and up and down the hallways. It was like someone was running around the house from door to door pounding with all of his or her might.

The police were called to come quickly. When they arrived, they found nothing. The noise had stopped. The fresh snow lay untouched, in drifts against the sides of the house. There were no footprints or disturbances of any kind. The police were baffled but could offer no explanation or comfort.

Other than batteries losing their power, and appliances that stopped working without reason (they usually became functional again after bit of time passed), constant problems with disappearing objects and ongoing difficulties with the electricity, things were pretty quiet for a long time. The kids went to school, played football and basketball, went to proms and lived an otherwise normal life as kids are meant to when they're growing up.

Then, one night in November of the year of her graduation, a sudden slamming and banging again woke them up. The kitchen cupboards were swinging wildly, causing the dishes inside to chatter. Her mother stood in the middle of the room with her hands on her hips for just a moment, then she carefully walked to each of the cupboard doors and closed them gently. The noise stopped. As she turned, there was a movement detected by the mere displacement of the air beside them.

Through the years, the spirit of this man never harmed them. There was a feeling of deep sorrow that sometimes flooded the house for days at a time, then it would be gone as if it had never been there. As time passed, they caught occasional glimpses of him on the main stairway, in the library, the dining room, the kitchen and by the window in our parents' bedroom. Sometimes there would be a book missing from a table, or a chair pushed aside. Footsteps often accompanied the frigid cold and alerted them of his arrival again.

They did discover that there is supposed to be a river that runs under the house from the old mine. Could this spirited activity be the haunted souls of the miners lost on that fateful morning? Alternatively, is it the spirit of Charles Stakel, the mining superintendent of the Barnes-Hecker who didn't show up for his daily inspection on November 3, 1926? Is it his ghost that cannot forgive his absence that day? Does he, in some way, blame himself for the tragedy?

After thoroughly researching the Barnes-Hecker Mine disaster and the Memoirs of Charles J. Stakel, I discovered he was a man loved by his friends, family, and employees. He went on after the disaster to become respected professionally, politically, and personally. I don't believe the restless spirit at North Lake is Charles Stakel. So many owners have come and gone through the years and each of them, perhaps, have left their faded footsteps and shadows in the old mansion.

In fact, is the house haunted to this day? The last reporting of a haunting in the mansion was from the memories of a young family who had lived there as children many years ago. Has the restless spirit that inhabited the mansion now gone on to another life, or does it remain, or was it ever there at all? Is this another mysterious happening that occurs without explanation or care for our human curiosity?

The North Lake Mansion

In The Woods, Somewhere along M-28

Many unexplained sights have been noted along the drive between Ishpeming and the Copper Country. Startled drivers and passengers have told stories of unexpected lights in the sky and huge man-like beasts dashing in front of their vehicles. Black bear, deer, and an occasional moose are rational explanations but what about this odd story told to me by two young teachers?

Mid-April found Mark and Tina returning from spring break to their teaching posts in the Copper Country. They had driven from Ann Arbor that morning and they were both tired. They stopped in Marquette about 9:30 p.m. for some fast food. They considered getting a motel until morning, but with the weather being perfect and the enticing thought that they could spend the night in their own bed – they urged themselves on.

M-28 wrapped through the highlands between Marquette and L'Anse. Jack pines and birch trees lined the highway as the couple headed due west. The only radio station they could receive played country music mile after mile through the darkness. It faded in and out and then gradually faded away, leaving static in its place. No oncoming traffic appeared that night, just relentless mile after mile of darkness. The headlights offered only the gray-paved highway in front of them and left blackness behind.

Over time, lights started flickering in the trees. They weren't noticed immediately and if they were, Mark might have thought they could have been passing an isolated camp or house. Then unexpectedly, lights appeared as if dozens of flashlights were following the car. Next, they appeared on both sides of the road. Faster and faster they came racing to keep up with the car and its occupants.

Mark was frightened by the sudden onslaught of the bouncing orbs. Tina gasped for breath as the lights surrounded them. Mark could no longer see the road; he had no choice but to stop. As he pulled to the side of the highway, he shouted for Tina to lock her door. They held on to each other as the bouncing orbs danced around them.

Then... they were gone. Silence filled the vacated air. Mark and Tina were shaken. They couldn't stay where they were, wherever that was, so Mark pulled back onto the road. Tina pulled closer to her husband. Mark pressed on the accelerator, gathering speed, anxious to recognize any landmark. The car raced west.

Suddenly, again, the lights appeared in the woods ahead of them, off to the right, less than a quarter of a mile away. They hovered just over the trees a few minutes then dropped below the tree line and disappeared. Mark stopped. He didn't want to pass the objects in the woods. Mark wondered how far they had traveled since leaving Ishpeming. He looked at his watch. 10:35. They had to be somewhere between Michigamme and Three Lakes. They should be able to find some help. There wasn't a signal on their cell phone but Mt. Shasta, the old restaurant should be along here somewhere, or had they passed it?

Mark moved back onto the highway and made a U-turn to head back east. Isolation haunted them as they again saw the lighted orbs ahead – this time in the center of the road. Mark slammed on the brakes. Tina buried her face in her hands. Mark, frantically jerked the car into another U-turn and hit the accelerator racing west as he watched the road behind them and in front of them and around them. His hands finally relaxed on the wheel as they crossed the bridge in Alberta. Another few miles and they reached L'Anse. They drove around the bay into the outskirts of Baraga where the lights of the Best Western motel beckoned to them. Safety.

The pair never discussed the strange lights among friends or co-workers. They seldom brought up the subject even between themselves. About two months later, there appeared in the weekly newspaper, an article describing the experience of a couple returning from a weekend in Marquette. The couple described seeing several orbs of light traveling at high speeds in the night sky near Michigamme.

Besides passenger cars, recreational vehicles and semi-trucks, what exactly travels M-28 between Marquette and L'Anse?

Men say in this midnight hour,
the disembodied have power,
to wander as it liketh them,
by wizard oak and fairy stream.
　　　　　　~ William Motherwell (1797-1835)

The Talking Board,
Silver City/White Pine

Perhaps all books about ghosts should include at least one story about the twilight world of the "talking board"– the Ouija. This particular tale one is one of the better ones I have heard. Eight people witnessed this event and they are willing to authenticate it.

It was the weekend of Halloween. Several people had gathered together for a party at a small abandoned house in the White Pine area. One of the guests, Sandy, an attractive thirty-year-old, had brought a Ouija board with her from Wisconsin. Several of the women expressed an interest in "getting it to work." As they gathered around the kitchen table, the board was placed in the center. It was cracked and yellowed with age. Tarot symbols circled the outside edges. When asked about it, Sandy replied that it was something her mother had bought at a flea market in Milwaukee about fifteen years before.

"Anyway, who cares about the age of the thing, let's see if it works," she declared as she joined the others at the table. Four of the women placed their fingertips lightly on the planchette. Nothing happened. They waited silently. Suddenly, the planchette flew from one letter to the next. It quickly spelled the name "Ada." It stopped.

"So, okay, who is Ada?" asked Sandy.

"Shhh," muttered someone.

"Be quiet," said a shaky voice.

"Did you make it move?" accused Sandy.

"No," whispered Cindy, "You did."

"I didn't"

"Then who did?"

Then it started again. Quickly and deliberately moving to spell out d-a-n-g-e-r –g-a-s. It spelled this out too many times to count. Over and over again, d-a-n-g-e-r-g-a-s.

The women soon tired of the repetitive nature of the board and called it quits.

After the women rejoined their husbands, the men asked how many spirits had they contacted.

"Someone called Ada told us to beware of gas," grumbled Sandy.

Her husband Kevin's face turned white. "Ada?" he sharply questioned.

"Yeah, Ada," Sandy repeated.

He turned to his wife, "Get your jacket … we're leaving … now!"

"Right now? Why?" she asked.

One of the men interrupted, "God, what's the matter? You afraid of spooks or something?"

Kevin stopped and stood in the doorway to the porch. "Yeah, I'm afraid of spooks. Back in '99, my best friend lived in this place. He committed suicide in the shed by letting the car run. His wife and kid died too from the fumes seeping into the house under the back door. The kid's name was Ada."

The party broke up. The Ouija board was left on the kitchen table. The house sat deserted at the end of the two-track lane.

About two months later, it mysteriously burned down.

Strangely enough, that summer when Sandy returned to her hometown for a visit, she discovered the same Ouija board in the window of a downtown antique shop. A woman, who left her name as Ada, had brought in the Ouija board several weeks ago.

Sandy caught a shiver down her back, but bought it anyway thinking to herself; it's only a game …

Isn't it?

No Will-o'-the Wisp, mislight thee;

Nor snake, or slow worm bite thee

But on they way

Nor making astray

Since ghost there's none to affright thee

> *– Robert Herrick (1591-1674)*

The Dog Meadow Lights, Paulding

The White Pine and Silver City area brings us as far west as we will journey on this road tour. It is now late fall as I write and early snows squalls can create mischief along these long, lonely stretches of highway. Passing through Bergland and Bruce Crossing on M-28, we turn on US-45 to Paulding and Watersmeet.

For years, my husband and I had heard stories of the Paulding Lights. Both of us were curious to discover what the truth really was concerning this Michigan mystery. The phenomenon is located off US-45, just four miles north of Watersmeet. You need to turn on Robbins Pond Road. We followed the gravel road to a large boulder and a barricade. Both prevented further travel to the valley below. Power lines followed the old roadbed down to the valley and back up to the hill on the other side only to disappear in the distance. Scrub brush, pine, and maple trees stand guard along both sides of the view. A small river cuts the valley in half.

Arriving about twenty minutes before twilight, silence and anticipation enveloped us as we watched the distant hilltop. Another car joined our watch … then another. Soon cars lined both sides of the road. People walked to the boulder and stopped. They stood in small groups watching … waiting. And then, there it was! A distant spark on the horizon growing larger and larger, coming closer and closer. Then slowly, as if burning out, it disappeared into nothing.

Hushed whispers filled the group of people that had grown to nearly fifty. Nervous giggles echoed along the road while hesitant bursts of hushed laughter spread among the gathering. Suddenly, it was there again. In the distance, near the top of the hill, the small pure white light once again started its journey to the valley; this time it appeared larger and brighter and then just as suddenly … it was gone.

Speculation grew in the crowd. Questions were being asked of one another. Stories of previous visits were passed between the assembly. Some men pushed forward with flashlights, determined to walk to the top of the distant hill to investigate. They left, disappearing into the darkness, leaving only the blobs of light from their flashlights as a guide to their progress and soon, those were gone too.

Again, the lights appeared, two this time, dancing it seemed, along the power line. Impossible, your brain told you. The crowd inhaled breathlessly in suspense, all eyes glued to the phenomenon that appeared to travel as far as the river below. At that point, the lights squeezed themselves into one and slowly receded into the distant hill.

The men who had disappeared into the darkness returned, their lights bouncing up the old roadbed. They had seen nothing. "Nothing was visible from the road bed… the river is too large to cross." Their voices drifted off into the crowd.

We listened to the stories of others who had been here several times. The mysterious light fascinated each of them. A regular visitor to the site told us Ripley's Believe It or Not has offered a $1 million reward to anyone who could solve the mystery. I spoke with Ripley Entertainment Inc. according to Edward Meyer-VP of Exhibits & Archives, "No, this is not true. We have never had any interest in these lights, nor have we ever offered rewards for information or any other phenomena."

Often called ghostlights, will o' the wisps, spooklights, and earthlights, they generally appear in the south and western United States. Usually described as a glowing ball or balls of lights, they often appear in every color of the rainbow. They are often said to exhibit some bizarre behaviors, such as vanishing or splitting in two when something approaches them too closely, sparkling or remaining stationary. They usually appear in a fixed location and appear at set times such as twilight or sunset, but they rarely appear in rain, snow or fog.

L.C. Krause of Obiway Paranormal told us that there are "many theories and legends surrounding these mysterious lights. Some attempts at explaining the lights include reflections from nearby traffic or towns, gas from marshlands, continental drift…" Common folktales from the locals include the tale the spirit of an old railroad engineer swinging his lantern, a ghostly Indian brave searching for his war club, a phantom train, UFO's, or Pancake Joe dancing on the power lines in protest to the power company running lines across his property. (Although the lights have been here since memories have recorded them, so there goes the Pancake Joe theory!)

The trip was well worth the effort. We enjoyed seeing the lights. They are truly a mystery. But most of all, we thoroughly enjoyed meeting the many people who gathered there in that spot to share thoughts and ideas and speculation as to what on earth is the Paulding Light–if indeed, it is earthly.

The Paulding Light as it slowly appears just after dusk.

The Bride-To-Be,
A Folk Tale of the Western U.P.

Driving south from Watersmeet, a stop at local restaurant was rewarded with this wonderful story.

A vacant church nearby has been the focal point of a haunting by a young woman said to have killed herself in the 1840's. According to local legend, the small church was abandoned in the 1900's because of the haunting. Its location needs to remain unidentified for the privacy of the surrounding community.

The story begins when a beautiful young woman in her early '20's became engaged to a prominent businessman's son. The young man courted the young woman according to the custom of the day. Finally, she accepted his proposal of marriage. Blessed by the parents of both youngsters, the families planned a large wedding to be held in the local parish hall after the spring planting. However, a number of times during this period, the young man would fail to meet his fiancée at the appointed times for social occasions. Although his excuses were meager, his soon-to-be-bride accepted them with a sad smile crossing her lips.

After several of these cancellations and as the wedding day grew closer, she began to get somewhat impatient with her young man.

On the night of the Spring Solstice Dance, an important social occasion for the community, and just two weeks before the wedding, once again the young man sent a message to his beloved that he would be unable to attend that evening's festivities.

Upon receiving the message, the young lady flew into a temper. "Fiddles be done, I'll dance with the devil tonight for I'll not sit home again!" Her parents wrung their hands and her father forbade her to leave the house, but she dressed in her best gown and started to walk to the parish hall. Friends and neighbors remember passing her and asked if she would like to ride with them in their buggies. No, she nodded, and continued on her way. Her slippers and petticoat were already soiled when a handsome black buggy pulled close. Gratefully, finally she accepted the offer of a ride. That night she gaily danced with her handsome escort who twirled her about in her satin slippers and he with his… cloven hooves.

She ran from the hall to the church, crying and tearing at her hair. She madly climbed the bell tower steps and reaching the top, without hesitation, she jumped from the bell tower. The townspeople found her broken body the following morning. That same day, a cloven hoof print was found burned into the wooden floor of the parish hall. You can still see it there, even today.

The legend is told that the ghost of the young woman can still be seen running from the parish hall to the church or standing on the ledge of the bell tower, especially during the spring solstice.

Every town has an abandoned church, and nearly all have a parish hall with wooden floors. On a stormy night, see if you can't get one of the locals to tell you the story of the young bride-to-be who danced with the devil.

Throw a key at an apparition. It will disappear.

West Wind Resort, Between Watersmeet and Iron Mountain

Driving southeast on US-2 revealed many abandoned Ma-and-Pa resorts that sat with vacant windows, watching the passing tourists.

This old resort is just one of many that used to dot the Upper Peninsula. Most of them are gone now, replaced by modern motels and convenience stores. However, there are some that remain and are fully booked for the season with spirits that return year after year, to relax, of course. Where else would a spirit go to take a break? It is said that Old Deerfield, located in Gulliver, is one of the resorts that still retains the flavor of the early '40's. It has a spirit or two of its own surprisingly enough, in cabin 24!

The West Wind Resort was located between Watersmeet in Michigan and the Land O' Lakes area in Wisconsin. The old resort was built in the 1940's and although remodeled and refurbished several times, it retained its early '40's flavor. Twenty-five log cabins lined the inland lakeshore like a string of pearls, but painted pink, they seemed unlikely candidates for membership in the jack pine forest behind them. Marlene and Al pulled into the resort restaurant around 3:00 in the afternoon on a warm Saturday in late July. Their reservation for two weeks of fishing and relaxing was about to begin. The couple was in their early

'40's and both worked in the factories of Flint and Detroit. They definitely needed this vacation.

The owner, Shirley and her husband, John, greeted them as they walked in the screened-in porch of the resort's restaurant. "You two must be tired after that long ride. Come on in and have a cool drink," invited Shirley, a huge smile plastered on her face.

John offered his hand as he said, "I'll get your keys for you and meet you at the cottage." The screen door banged behind his departure.

"It's number 24," Shirley called to him as he walked down the porch steps.

Two waitresses at the end of the snack bar looked at each other and gave Shirley a long stare.

"What's with you two?" she said as she handed an iced tea and a Coke across the counter.

"You're kidding, Shirl. Cabin 24?" the stringy–haired blonde asked.

Shirley gave the two a look that would kill as they headed back to the kitchen.

"Don't mind those two," she said as she wiped the countertop.

"You had problems with that cabin, or is it haunted?" Laughed Al. Marlene gave him a nudge with her elbow.

"No, no problems except an occasional bat finding its way in."

"Boy, I am hot," said Marlene as she pushed her hair back behind her ears. "Can we go now? I would really like a shower."

"Sure, honey, and what do I owe you?" he asked Shirley, as he pulled open his billfold.

"On the house," she smiled. "Come on, I'll walk you over to

your home for the next two weeks."

The lake was a dark cobalt blue, small waves licked at the shoreline as they walked to the cottage. It squatted beneath a few large white pines that used to cover this area. They were long gone now due to heavy logging in the early part of the century.

"Al," Marlene murmured as she pulled at this sleeve. "You forgot our suitcases and stuff."

"Hell, yes I did. I'll be right back," he called over his shoulder as he walked back to the restaurant parking lot.

Marlene and Shirley walked up the log steps and entered the screened-in front porch. Already the mosquitoes were gathering at the screens. They heard a sharp bang from the back of the cottage. John came out to greet them. "Damn toilet," he said. "Going to have to replace it. But don't you worry any, I'll get it working in no time. I have to run into town for a part. It will work for now. I'll get back to it in the morning."

Finally, Marlene and Al were alone. They glanced at the old log walls and rough rugs on the floor.

"We'll make the best of it, Al, and it might not be all that bad. We are just plain tired," she remarked as she headed for the shower.

"God, it is in the middle of nowhere for sure," mumbled Al to himself as he unpacked the suitcases and put on a pot of coffee. "It's quaint, all right," he muttered, stressing the Q. "It's almost too damn old to be quaint."

That night they strolled along the shoreline for a bit, before turning toward the restaurant for dinner. They returned to number 24 well after dark. They noticed as they passed the other cabins that most of them looked vacant, except one or two down by the playground at the far end of the resort. Funny, there wasn't anyone around, no kids chasing fireflies or porch–sitters for conversation.

The murmur of the west wind through the pines lulled them to sleep. They fished the following day well into the evening. Apparently, while they were gone John had fixed the plumbing so the sounds of gurgling and creaking finally stopped. At the end of the third day, they were both brown as berries and admitted to themselves that, in spite of the lack of modern conveniences of any kind, they were relaxing somewhat, although Marlene's face had seemed to tighten around her lips and John's conversation had become a little sharp. That night, while sitting on the porch as they watched a huge bonfire across the lake, Al asked Marlene if she didn't think it was odd that they didn't see any other people around.

Marlene took her time answering. "Funny you should mention that. It is kinda weird. I know Shirley told me they were fully booked, this week being mid-July and all. Speaking of weird … as I was sweeping the floor yesterday when you were down at the dock, I heard the screen door open and close. I thought it was you. But it wasn't."

"Who was it?"

She answered slowly, "A man carrying a shotgun."

"Who was he?"

"I never had a chance to ask."

"Because?"

"He disappeared. He just sort of melted away into nothing."

"Nothing, eh?" Al leaned back into the rose printed chair. "Anything else, honey?"

"Well," Marlene said as she took a deep breath, "that isn't the first time something has happened around here."

"Like what else?"

"Haven't you noticed the lights being on when we come home

at night? I didn't turn them on. Or the shower running and you are not in it. Or tell me you haven't noticed the cupboard doors opening and closing as I make coffee or a sandwich."

"Fact is sweetheart, I've been too busy noticing my own little 'nothings'. I was cleaning fish yesterday, out in front by the lake. A guy walked up to me and asked where the owners were. I told him they were probably up at the restaurant. He walked around me and down the beach, and – Marlene – he disappeared into nothing, too."

"And, baby, that's not everything. I also caught a guy wearing coveralls walking out of our kitchen and out the front porch door. It scared me because I couldn't see his head. I don't think he had one. I tried calling out to him but I lost my voice. I was shaking all over." Marlene's face turned white. She twisted the wedding rings on her finger. As she looked toward the front door, she asked, "Do you remember the stories we heard about the hauntings down in Land O' Lakes, Wisconsin? The stories about that house that was so haunted, the one that is burned down now. You know, the famous one?"

"Do you mean, Summerwind?"

"Yes, that's it."

"And, Al, those lights, you know the meadow lights. Aren't they just north of us in Watersmeet?"

"Yeah, I think so."

"Could those incidents be part of what is going on here?"

"I think that light up in Watersmeet is a lot of baloney. As for that haunted house, it's gone now. I don't see how that stuff could affect this place."

They stayed close together that day. They were leery of the incidents that surrounded them. They talked about leaving but decided to wait until the next day before making any decision.

The following morning found the lake covered with fog. It seemed to creep through the pines and spread like a film over the shoreline.

"No fishing today," said Al.

"Maybe the sun will melt it away later in the morning," Marlene remarked as she fried eggs and sausage for breakfast. Al stood in the living room, holding his cup of coffee while watching the fog through the large picture window. Suddenly, he jumped back. "God!" he cried out.

There in the window was a man with a large cloth, apparently washing the outside of the window.

Al strode to the front porch hollering as he went, "What in the hell do you think you're doing? Are you crazy? You scared the living daylights out of me!" He shouted as he walked around the corner of the cottage, then stopped.

No one was there. No ladder - and you would need a ladder to reach that window. No bucket. Not a thing. Al looked around to the backside of the cabin. Nothing. He walked all around the place. No one was there. Only the dripping of moisture off the tree limbs filled the silence around him.

Marlene and Al later sat at a log-fashioned table, facing John and Shirley. It was raining out. Thunder lodged a complaint in the distance. The lights flickered as Al confronted John with stories of the mysterious happenings at the cottage that week.

"Now you tell us!" His voice punctuated the atmosphere. "What is going on in this place? We want some explanations or we want our money back!"

John got up from the table and walked to the cash register. He returned with several bills in his hand. He counted them out as he laid them on the table.

"We're sorry this has happened. You're not the first to encounter old Cabot." Said John.

"Old Cabot?"

"He used to be the caretaker here back in the early '40's...," offered Shirley, "...but he died a rather horrible death down at cabin 24."

"And exactly how did he die?" Al demanded.

"He killed himself. He shot himself in the head." John muttered.

"Well why on earth did you give us cabin 24? Why us? You have lots of empty ones." Marlene exclaimed.

"It doesn't matter which one we assigned you. Cabot visits all of them." replied John.

"Is that why there are no other guests here?" Asked Marlene.

"Yeah, pretty much," said Shirley. "Word's gotten out that the place is haunted. When we bought it, we didn't know the history. We've tried real hard to make a go of it but most people stay a night or two and then leave."

"We've pretty much given up," John said, "We're going to close it down and take the loss. You two have been our last reservation for the season. We might get a couple of drive-ins but they usually stay the night and leave at the light of day."

Shirley poured another round of coffee while saying she would like to keep the restaurant open, but John wanted to leave this part of the country for good. He had had enough of jack pines and tourists and spirits of headless men.

Today, the West Wind Resort is no longer there. About a year after John and Shirley left, the property was purchased at a bank foreclosure sale by a developer from Milwaukee. The cabins and restaurant were demolished in preparation for a resort condominium development. To this day, the land remains vacant.

The Traveling Poltergeist, Iron Mountain

I interviewed the two girls and their mother for this story about two years ago. They agreed to tell this tale in exchange for complete anonymity. I agreed. This type of spirit often becomes attached to an object or member of the family it once held dear. Time usually cures this type of haunting.

This story begins in a one-and-a-half story bungalow in a small suburb of Detroit during the fall of 1978. After the death of her first husband, Laura and her two daughters moved into this small house and were in the process of fixing it up to make it a real home.

Paint buckets formed paths through the house and torn-up carpeting covered the front lawn. Renovations kept the small family busy during the first months of occupation, but finally everything was finished. The main floor had a tiny living room, dining room, a main bedroom, and another smaller bedroom for the youngest daughter, Kim. The stairway to upstairs was in the center of the house and completely enclosed. At the top of the stairs was a small bedroom that belonged to the oldest daughter, Mary. Another bedroom was located down the long narrow hallway. It was completely paneled in knotty pine and Laura used it as a sewing room.

A recreation room was located in the basement. It, too, was paneled in knotty pine. It was a comfortable room filled with a sofa, overstuffed chairs, a television, stereo, and a player piano that Laura had had since childhood. There was a small room off the stairway that was used for crafts and painting, and a laundry room was across the hall.

One evening after work, Laura went to the basement, to do some laundry. The radio was playing the Carpenters' song, "We've Only Just Begun," and she hummed along with the music as she folded clothes. She was about to start upstairs when she heard Mary come in the front door.

"Hi Mom!" Mary called.

"Down in the basement, Honey." Laura answered.

Suddenly, as Mary started downstairs to her mother, loud uncontrolled laughing burst from inside the wall next to her. Startled, Mary turned too quickly and tumbled down the steps. Unhurt, she clutched at the railing as the earsplitting laughter continued. Louder and louder. It echoed down the stairs as if it were running back and forth, like a maddened old woman.

"Stop it! Stop it!" Laura shouted.

Mary cringed next to the bottom step and the wall.

Then it stopped. Laura and Mary stared at each other. They ran up the steps to the living room.

"What in hell was that?" Laura asked, trying to catch her breath.

"Mom, I am scared to death. Where did that come from?"

Laura immediately called her brother-in-law, Mike, and told him what had happened. It took Mike fifteen minutes to reach the front door of Laura's house. He and his neighbor, John, searched the entire house from top to bottom. They found nothing, absolutely nothing to account for the strange laughter. Mike suggested it might have been noises from the new furnace recently installed or a kink in the plumbing. Laura and Mary were finally persuaded that it was some quirk in the house.

Things went on smoothly for awhile. Kim entered the fourth grade that fall and Mary, a tenth grader, discovered basketball. Laura continued her home advertising business with unexpected success.

One night while Laura and the girls were sitting in the kitchen having a late dinner, sounds of the player piano drifted up through the heat ducts. Kim kneeled down by the duct to listen. The sounds stopped. Mary sat in her chair, stiff as a board.

"Ok, Mom, here we go again. That's not the furnace or the plumbing, is it?"

Laura shook her head, "No … that's my piano."

"How can it play by itself?" asked Kim.

"It can't, dummy. We have a ghost."

"Mary, don't scare Kim. It's not a ghost, Kim. It's just a little quirk in our house."

"Right…" answered Mary, "… a little quirk."

The piano started again, another Carpenters' song, Laura couldn't think of the name of it. She told the girls to stay put as she started down the basement steps. Her hands were sweating and her heart racing as she stood on the bottom step watching the keys move in perfect time. She moved closer. The music stopped. An icy cloud of air filled the area around her. She touched a key it was like a cube of ice. She could see her breath as she backed away, turned and ran up the stairs. She noticed the kitchen clock was blinking green. On. Off. On. Off.

"Mom, you look like you've seen a ghost!" cried Mary.

"Mommy!" Kim cried as she ran to her mother and wrapped her arms around her.

"It's okay girls. I promise you everything is okay. I think we have the makings of the spirit of my Aunt Martha visiting and she would never ever hurt us."

"But Aunt Martha is dead," said Mary, "and has been dead for like four years?"

"Well…" answered Laura slowly, "…lots of times, people come back to make sure everything is going okay. You both remember what a busybody Aunt Martha was …" Suddenly the refrigerator door opened. They watched in amazement as a bottle of catsup fell on the floor; the door closed quietly again. "And, remember," Laura continued hesitantly, "Aunt Martha loved to play the piano."

Aunt Martha or not, life continued somewhat quietly in the small house after the refrigerator incident, with the exception of the spirit's preoccupation with clocks. The clock in the kitchen would stop running every Thursday at 3 o'clock in the afternoon. This was strange because it was a ten-day clock and was about fifty years old. It had never stopped early before. The clock in the laundry room would often have a reddish glow as one of the family came down the stairs and the color would gradually fade as they ignored it. The clock in Laura's room sometimes ticked so loudly that she moved it to the bathroom closet. It made so much noise there that one night she shouted, "SHUT UP!" It did, and never ticked loudly again.

If it was Aunt Martha's ghost, apparently correct identification of her spirit led to a lack of pranks in the small bungalow, which was clearly acceptable to the occupants. Even Kim adjusted to the fact that they might have the ghost of an old aunt visiting them. She never told a soul. After all, you would really have to be a little crazy to admit a belief in ghosts, wouldn't you?

Sometimes when Laura or one of the girls would be on the steps leading upstairs, the window shade on the window at the top of the steps would fly up and wrap itself tightly, then spring all the way down its full length. Several new shades didn't remedy the problem. A small giggle could be heard after each shady incident. A disgusted, angry cry of "Aunt Martha, stop it!" only elicited another laugh and the rustle of a dress in need of a hem.

In 1982, Laura remarried and moved to the city of Ludington, home of the Lake Michigan car ferries. She never gave another thought to Aunt Martha when she and the girls left the house that had caused them so many hours of distress. Laura was glad to put Aunt Martha behind them. They moved into a large A-frame near the lake, and Laura hung the familiar clocks throughout the house. It was a warm day in July, about three months after they had moved in, when Aunt Martha let it be known that she, too, seemed to have taken up residence in the new place. At least Laura hoped it was Aunt Martha.

It started when the family held a birthday celebration for her new husband Clay's, youngest son Andy. At the end of a day filled with fun, several helium balloons remained floating about in the kitchen, hallway, and bedrooms. The family was sitting at the kitchen table finishing up the cake and ice cream when Laura watched a blue and silver balloon lower itself through the hallway door and came straight at the group. She let a small cry escape her lips as she pointed at the strange phenomena.

"What's wrong?" her husband asked. Laura pointed at the balloon.

"It's just caught in a draft," he answered.

"Of course. How silly of me," Laura laughed nervously. Although she had told him about the antics of the ghost at her old house, he clearly thought this was the product of his new family's imagination.

"Mom! It's gotta be Aunt Martha! Look!" shouted Kim.

The balloon stopped right over Andy's head. Andy swiped at its string and the balloon flew in a straight line towards the door and down the hallway. Clay quickly followed and stopped dead when he saw the balloon deflate and land on his and Laura's bed. Laura and the kids had followed closely behind him.

"Wow!" exclaimed Andy.

Clay turned to Laura and touched her chin lightly. "Now, I believe in Aunt Martha. What else does she do?"

Laura let out a long drawn-out breath, "You'll see."

Slowly, once again, the clocks started to behave strangely and the piano, now kept on the sun porch, continued to play, but only when no one was home. After brief absences – to get the mail or groceries or pick up laundry, family members complained to each other of hearing its tunes as they approached the front porch. It always stopped when the front door was opened.

In 1988, while the family was visiting the Upper Peninsula, there was a terrible lightning storm. Lightning struck the A-frame and the jolt of electricity went through the television, knocked the clock in the kitchen off the wall and cracked the glass. Shortly after that, Laura painted the clock green and had the glass repaired. Soon the clock was stopping every Wednesday at 3:30 p.m., the time when Andy left school and started home. Laura and Clay, finally tired of dealing with the old clock, sold it at a yard sale as they got ready to move to Upper Michigan. The spirit of Aunt Martha appeared to leave with the sale of the clock.

They moved to Iron Mountain in the spring of 1997 and everything remained quiet – that is, until the first Christmas in their new home when Laura carefully placed her collection of Christmas Villages on top of the dining room cupboards. The little houses had lights inside. Small strings of lights traced the outline of the miniature trees. There was a skating rink that played music, a beautiful church, a replica of the Sand Point Lighthouse in Escanaba, a tavern, and about fifteen other assorted pieces.

One night, when Clay was ill with the flu, Laura noticed the lights in the villages would not turn on. About a week later, when

Clay was better, he asked Laura why the lights were not on in the Christmas village. She told him they were burnt out. He turned the switch on. They lit up perfectly. Laura looked at them, then at Clay and whispered, "Aunt Martha?" No sooner were the words said then the lights went out again, that is, all but the church lights. That was impossible. They were all on the same line. Clay walked over to the village and said very nicely, "Aunt Martha, please turn on the Christmas lights." And, she did.

For eleven years, Laura and Clay have lived in their new home. Occasionally they hear slippers shuffling down the long hallway of the upper floor, and Laura has been startled awake by the sense of someone standing over their bed. One time, Clay thought he felt Laura tucking the blankets in around him. It wasn't Laura. Visitors complain of seeing a white mass dash down the hallway on their way to the bathroom, and once in awhile, a picture can be found hanging upside down. But for these few things, Aunt Martha's spirit only seems to play pranks when the family is reunited for a holiday or special occasion.

Could Aunt Martha be identified as a poltergeist? It is true that a poltergeist may appear when there are young people around. They love to play practical jokes on everyone and even enjoy scaring the bejebbes out of someone occasionally. This spirit has been with Laura's family for twenty-six years and although seldom heard from these days, Laura and Clay are always watchful for any new activity. This year the grandchildren will be home for the holidays.

As to the laughter in the walls those many years ago, the family never found an adequate explanation and it was never repeated.

Another Haunted House, Menominee

Driving southeast along US-2, turning south at Powers on US 41 brings us into Menominee, where Dennis and Marge have just recently purchased their dream house.

This is the perfect house for a haunting. It really looks the part. Although I only visited once to meet with the new owners, I was impressed with their honesty and their fear.

The house was over a hundred years old. It was a large house with fifteen to twenty rooms, that is, counting the ones you could find. The downstairs was a twisted maze consisting of a formal entry, a library with a massive fireplace, a study, formal living room and dining room, a large pantry, kitchen, maids' quarters and a solarium of sorts. The upstairs had seven bedrooms. They were lined up on either side of ten-foot wide hallways. This hallway had two floor-to-ceiling windows overlooking a huge stone fountain topped with angels in the garden below.

Huge maple trees and a fieldstone fence wrapped around the property that squatted on a ledge overlooking Lake Michigan. At one time, the mansion was owned by a pair of sisters, who had left a Catholic convent after many years of service. It is unclear if their family had been the original owners.

Marge and Dennis bought the old place for a good price. They intended to make it into a bed and breakfast. They had heard the stories about the house, but they were young and full of excitement and energy. Marge's father, who was retired from the Coast Guard, was a very cynical man. He hated the house the first time he saw it. He refused to walk into it. I interviewed Marge and Dennis at the house on a sunny morning in mid-July. We sat on the back porch, sipping on tall glasses of iced tea in the warm summer heat.

Marge said the mysterious happenings started very slowly. "Just little things at first," she began, "One day I was baking pies and the kitchen door kept opening. I closed it several times. There wasn't a wind outside and it finally got me mad. I slammed it shut and put a chair next to it. It stopped, but out of the corner of my eye I thought I saw a man walking through the kitchen and into the dining room hallway. I turned to see him more clearly, but he was gone. There was nothing there," she said quietly as she leaned toward her husband. She looked back to me "I got shivers all over. Then, as I returned to the kitchen, I watched the back door push the chair open again. I ran from the kitchen to find Dennis, who was in the back entrance hanging wallpaper."

Dennis continued, "We had started to remodel within the first month of moving in. One day, I was working on removing wallpaper from the front entrance, Marge was in the kitchen baking pies. Suddenly she came running in and grabbed me in a bear hug. She was shaking all over. She breathlessly told me what had just happened. I walked her back into the kitchen and sat her down at the old table. Then I told her of the many times I had seen a man walking up the front steps, only to disappear before he reached the door. I had also caught him sitting in the library one late afternoon in one of the overstuffed chairs. He held a book in his hands. He looked up at me, then melted into nothing. The book remained in the seat of the chair.

"We both decided that day that we really loved this old place and if that was the worst a spirit would do, we would stay. And, well, we are still here."

Marge interrupted, "But that's not to say we haven't had our moments of second thoughts. One day as I reached the second floor landing, I noticed the bedroom door at the top of the stairs was ajar and it felt like a cold wind was coming from it. I leaned in to see if a window was open. Instead, there was a woman, who was dressed a fashion reminiscent of the early 1900's, sitting in the rocking chair reading a book. I slammed the door closed and ran downstairs to find Dennis. I really used to panic, but we've gotten pretty used to them, haven't we, Denny?"

"Have we?" Dennis asked as he looked toward the hallway. 'Once in a while, things can get to you. Just last week when we came home from golfing, we found all of the books that were on the top shelf of the bookcase in our bedroom, in the center of the floor. This has happened before. When we first moved in, we would find all of the books from the bottom shelf of the bookcase piled in the center of the floor. Sometimes there would only be one book in the center of the room."

Marge laughed. "I used to say I spent a lot of time picking up after the kids. Now I have to pick up after ghosts."

"Marge laughs now," Dennis continued, "but there have been times when she would come running to find me, scared to death and shaking all over. Our daughter's dog won't come into the house at all. He cringes and balks when we try to get him through the door. There are dozens of things that have happened that we cannot explain, but we are not afraid anymore. We plan to find out who the ghosts are if we can."

"Let me know if you discover anything." I requested.

The small pond in front of the house reflected the golden rays of the setting sun. "It will be hot again tomorrow," I quietly remarked as I finished my tea and started down the porch steps. Dennis and

Marge followed me to my car. I turned to them and held out my hand, thanking them for having me. We promised to get together in another month and set a date and time. I waved goodbye as I drove down the long driveway and headed for home.

About six months ago, I tried to reach Dennis and Marge to see if they had discovered the identity of their spirit. The house was abandoned. The only evidence of its previous owners was a wheelbarrow lying on its side in the shrubbery next to the front porch.

" From ghoulies and ghosties and long-leggedy beasties and things that go bump in the night, Good Lord, deliver us!"
~ From an old Scottish prayer of obscure origin

The House of Ludington, Escanaba

Built in 1864, the historic House of Ludington, on Ludington Street in downtown Escanaba, is currently haunted by the colorful and eccentric previous owner, Harold C. (Pat) Hayes. He was meticulous, demanding perfection from not only himself and staff, but also his guests. While he ruled the House of Ludington for twenty-eight years, he was a less than pleasant boss who frequently fired his staff in a rage without cause. He was a cruel and underhanded man, who, when he died, left the hotel to his two mistresses. The only benefit his wife received from his death was his absence.

The historic House of Ludington, in downtown Escanaba.

According to the present owners and staff, his ghost continues to walk the long hallways, hotel rooms, the elevator, kitchens, and dining rooms of this landmark hotel to this day.

The following are true stories about the old hotel that I have gathered for your enjoyment. There are many more to be told. This requires a visit with the current owners, who enjoy relating their encounters with puzzling gushing toilets, haunted doorknobs, mysterious moving chandeliers, haunted crystal punch bowls, pulled-back bed covers, and enigmatic windows.

Please enter with caution, the wonderful House of Ludington.

The Picture

This tale comes to me from a former employee of the House of Ludington. As a young woman, she worked part-time at the old hotel earning money for college expenses. Because she is a prominent businesswoman in the area today, I have sworn never to reveal her identity. This story is told in her own words, with some descriptive help from me.

"It was mid-February, the time of year when snow-driven winds whip across Little Bay de Noc and up the main street of Escanaba. The wind skipped around corners and down the hallways of the House of Ludington the night that I had my first encounter with the ghost of Pat Hayes. Like a lot of other kids my age, I worked part-time at the hotel to help pay college expenses. That night I was bartending. Patrons used to tell stories about Pat Hayes, the flamboyant former owner. I wasn't easily frightened and the stories amused me.

"That night, because of blizzard conditions outside, the bar was full of laughing, chatting patrons. I soon ran out of ice. This meant I had to traverse a long, dimly lighted corridor to the ice machine. The wind howled and chased me down that hallway. Icy cold fingers gripped me as I turned the corner to the room where the ice machine was located. I felt as if I had been grabbed by an unseen force and held prisoner by a wall of ice. I struggled

*The appearing and disappearing
picture of Pat Hayes*

to fill my container. The hair on my neck was standing straight up on end and it felt like a cold hand on my spine was pushing me back down the length of the hall.

"On the wall, next to the doorway into the bar, was a huge oil portrait of Chef Pat Hayes cutting a loin of beef. I gasped in amazement. I had never noticed it there before. I don't know how I could have missed it. It was hanging under a glowing light so that whoever passed down that hallway couldn't miss it. Apparently, I had.

"I pushed through the doorway back to where the tinkling of glasses and laughter reached out warmly to greet me. I was sweating. I glanced back at the doorway to the hall and shivered.

'What's the matter, Kelly? You look like you've seen a ghost.' Laughter circled the bar.

'Well' I replied, '… you could have told me about that picture of Pay Hayes in the hallway. It scared the daylights out of me. When did the boss put that there?'

'What picture? Where in the hallway?' asked Gary, my boss, as he came from the dining room.

'Pat Hayes,' I said 'The picture of Pat Hayes.'

'There's no picture of Pat Hayes or anyone else hanging in the hallway. You've been working too hard, kid.'

'No! There is a picture of him in the hall by the doorway just outside of the bar! It's huge! I just saw it!'

'Come with me kid and show it to me.'

"I led the way through the tables and back to the doorway to the hallway.

"It's just here outside on the wall,' I said as I opened the heavy door. Nothing. There was nothing there. No picture. Just a blank wall. Not even a light on the wall. I knew I had seen a light.

"I have never forgotten that night. I forget now who it is was that told me several years later that an oil painting of Pay Hayes had been found behind piles of furniture on the third floor. It was the very same picture I had seen that night in the hallway. Today the picture is hanging in the hallway where I first saw it. If you are at the House of Ludington, ask one of the owners or wait staff to show it to you. It's as big as life and to this day scares the daylights out of me when I see it hanging there in that hallway."

Caroline's Special Recipes

A talented lady, who created specialty dishes for the House of Ludington's special events many years ago, related this story to me. Although she had heard the many tales of the ghost of Pat Hayes and his antics, she was not a woman to frighten easily. Since this occasion, she refused to return to work during the midnight hours. She has since moved to an Arizona retirement community.

Caroline worked in her office just off the kitchen and a few steps before the stairway down to the wine cellar. She often worked until two and three in the morning. Her encounter with the spirit of Pat Hayes took place during one of her late night sessions. A janitor and front desk person were also present that night on the main floor.

It was about 1:30 in the morning when she heard tremendous bumping and banging coming from the hallway outside her office. It sounded like chairs and tables were being pushed or dragged from the banquet room down the hallway, the same hallway where Kelly had encountered the mysterious picture of Pat Hayes. This tremendous noise went on for about ten, maybe fifteen minutes. Her office suddenly turned ice cold. A frigid mist crept under the door to the hallway.

The sounds increased in intensity to the point of making the door rattle on its hinges. She finally got up and opened the hall door to see what on earth was going on. The hall was vacant. No one was there. Nothing was there. Nothing but silence. Nothing but silence and cold chills that crept up her spine and made the hair on the back of her neck stand on end. A wall of frigid air followed her to the front desk where Jim was reading a magazine.

"No," he answered to her inquiry, he hadn't heard anything unusual.

The janitor had left around midnight, complaining of a terrible headache. The two of them were alone as they walked down the long hallway and into the banquet room. The hallway lights kept going off and on, as if following their progress, while icy waves of air followed them. There was nothing there. The table and chairs were neatly arranged as they had been left after the last party.

Caroline insisted Jim return to her office with her to get her coat. As she left the hotel that night, she knew she would never work after dark again at the House of Ludington. Still, the sounds of moving furniture bumping against walls and scraping across floors in the midnight hours often startle guests in the Pub as they make their way to the restrooms. The chef, preparing for a special gathering of patrons, has often heard similar movements coming from the hallway.

The Haunted Hallway on the Second Floor
The second floor hallway has been the scene of many unusual

occurrences at the House of Ludington. During the first summer that the present owners, Ed and Suezel, had purchased the hotel, a young couple checked in with their nine-year-old son. Ed helped them carry their luggage to their room. The family cat met them at the elevator and followed them down the hall to room 205. The boy and the cat played in the hallway.

As the young couple and Ed stood in the hallway, the doorknob of room 205 began to shake. Harder and harder, it shook the entire door until they thought it would fall from its hinges.

This haunted second floor hallway of the House of Ludington. The light here is not a flashback. This picture was taken in February at 9:30 pm.

They all looked on in amazement.

"At that point," Ed said, "Suezel's cat took off down the hallway and has never returned to us. We found out later that it is living at a nearby neighbor's home. If someone had been on the inside of the door, it would have easily opened, as all of the doors open from the outside. We had no explanation to offer our guests. And we were thankful that nothing else happened during their stay with us."

However, that's not to say other things have not happened on the second floor. Some guests have complained of spending a sleepless night, tossing and turning, clutching the covers to their chest as sweeping cold drafts seem to swirl about, while others complain of their bed covers being pulled back by unseen phantoms. Chills chase visitors down the hallway to their rooms. TVs turn off and on by themselves, as do bedside lamps. Toilets flush and water faucets run, turned on and off by unseen hands.

Should you decide to spend the night in one of the rooms on the second floor, hang a small wind chime in a doorway. It will catch the spirit as it passes through and give you warning that Pat Hayes is nearby.

The Green Olives

Just recently there occurred an incident, that left everyone present mystified.

A new waitress, hired to work the Rotary Club luncheons, often needed to bring her four-year-old along with her. This bright little girl helps her mother carry water glasses and place napkins on the tables. When the guests arrive, she is put in her highchair, along with her Dora doll and assorted playthings. The highchair is always placed next to a large, round table. On the other side of the table is a tall buffet with shelves.

The little girl's favorite snack is green olives. Her mother always places the zip-lock bag full of this treat high on a shelf on the buffet until she finishes taking the order slips into the kitchen. On this particular day, she came around the corner to find her youngster eating the olives. She went into the kitchen and asked, "Did any of you give Susie her olive snack?" Everyone denied giving the youngster her treat. She returned to the Pub side of the hotel and asked, "Ed, did you give Susie her olives?"

Ed replied, "No, I've been right here. Why?" he asked. "What's up?"

"Susie is eating her olive treats, but I didn't give them to her and it's impossible for her to reach them. And, Ed, no one in the kitchen gave them to her either, so where did they come from?" she puzzled.

"Come on. We'll get to the bottom of this right now," said Ed firmly. They returned to the outer kitchen where the little girl remained in her highchair, happily eating olives.

Bending over the little girl, her mother calmly asked, "Now sweetheart, tell Mommy the truth. How did you get the olives? Who gave them to you?" Most of the staff had gathered around the highchair waiting for an answer. The Rotary Club members were unaware of the ongoing mystery.

The highchair and buffet. Note the orb on the top drawer of the buffet. An orb is thought to indicate the presence of spirit activity.

"The white ghost man did," she replied, as she calmly popped another olive into her rosebud mouth.

" Now, honey, tell me honestly, who gave you the olives?"

"Mommy!" she cried in exasperation. "The white ghost man gave me the whole bag from the shelf." Everyone shook their heads in amazement. Where had Susie ever gotten that idea?

Ed pulled her up from the highchair and with her mother following them, he brought Susie into the hallway where the picture of Pat Hayes hangs. "Is this the ghost man?" he asked. "Yes," she pointed, "he's a nice man. That's him." She smiled and ate another olive.

Hide and Seek

Ed tells this story as he stands in front of the elevator that often operates on its own time schedule. Could it be this elevator is a portal to the other world?

"One night when I was working alone, I stayed up waiting for the last guests to return. I may have fallen asleep for a bit. When I woke up, I heard the elevator going up. Then I heard it coming down. I watched the doors open, but there was no one there. Then it went back up.

"I ran up the stairway to the second floor. When I got to the elevator alcove, the elevator was going back down. I turned and ran back down the stairs and just as I reached the bottom step, the elevator doors were closing and – it was going up again! I waited for it to return to the second floor, but this time it went to the third floor! This kept up for about 15 to 20 minutes more. I couldn't run anymore. I just stood in front of the elevator and watched as it went on its merry way.

"Today I know that I played hide-and-seek with Pat Hayes that night. How do I know it was Pat Hayes? The glass elevator was his baby. He took great pride in it. It was the first glass elevator in the State of Michigan. Once in awhile, to this day, it will still light up and journey up and down. Sometimes it stops here on the main floor, but most frequently it stops at the second floor. If I listen carefully, I can hear the doors open and close.

"The wiring has all been checked several times. I have even run outside to watch it go up and then down. I guess Pat Hayes needs to make sure that it is still working. That first year we renovated, remodeled, repaired, repainted, and refurbished. Our goal remains the same today as it did when we first purchased the hotel, and that is to return it to its former splendor back in the 1900's, the way it used to be during the ownership of Pat Hayes. The House of Ludington is special and historical. It serves as a scrapbook of memories for so many people. Hopefully our guests and our ghosts are comfortable."

Ed and Suezel have many stories to tell you should you inquire. They love to share the wealth of hauntings they have experienced since purchasing the hotel. While you enjoy your dinner in the main dining room, watch carefully for the overhead chandeliers. On occasion they send a tinkle of sound throughout the room, and their lights dim by themselves. Ladies, a cautionary note - the ladies restroom located between the hallway and the pub, since being renovated, has also had a visitor or two of unknown origins.

May I suggest you try the Strawberry Salad for lunch. It is Suezel's secret recipe.

The Bonifas Theater, Escanaba

Ghosts seem to love the theater. I have discovered in my investigations that most theaters in the U.P. are haunted by phantom janitors or spirits of assorted cast members. Perhaps it's because it takes a real ham to haunt someplace for years and years, scaring the daylights out of people. I often think spirits have a real sense of humor and enjoy the reactions they get from the living souls they left behind.

The William Bonifas Memorial Auditorium and Gymnasium today known as the Bonifas Fine Arts Center was created when William Bonifas bequeathed funds to remodel the St. Joseph School and build a gymnasium and auditorium. The building was dedicated to his memory on April 24, 1938. The auditorium seated 600 and featured a beautiful stage. The gymnasium was considered one of the finest in the Upper Peninsula.

William's wife, Catherine, was often in attendance for events at the auditorium. Although she died on May 25, 1948, she remains a frequent visitor to the

The Bonifas Fine Arts Center in Escanaba.

Bonifas Theater today. The following stories are from past and present members of the Players de Noc, the theatrical group now based at the Bonifas Theater.

The Players de Noc were involved in a production of "Hello Dolly" when I first introduced myself. They were generous with their time, their stories, and patient with me poking my nose in and about their wonderful theater.

A former director joined me in the last row of seats as I watched rehearsals. She leaned toward me and began telling me about one of the curious incidents that had happened to her and that all too frequently plague the theater itself.

"Cast members know not to work behind the sets during rehearsal," she explained. "It's not only noisy but also distracting to see shadows through windows and doorways. It was during rehearsals of 'Murder at Howard Johnsons,' that I saw a shadow of movement behind a set window. I stopped the rehearsal and I told the people there to stop moving behind the set. Everyone there agreed that no one was behind the sets.

"We continued, and it happened again. This time there was movement behind two windows about five feet apart from each other. Once more I stopped rehearsal and adamantly told whomever it was to get out from behind the set. We continued on again, until I and five other cast members saw a figure walk from stage left to stage right, then stop to look out the window at us. It was a faded figure of a woman in clothing from the early 1900's. She was wearing a large brimmed, veiled hat.

"My heart pounded against my chest. I could barely breath. *Calm down,* I said to myself. *It's just Catherine.* Needless to say, we were all upset by the apparition. We found it impossible to continue practice that evening," she concluded.

At that moment, one of the costume designers joined us in the darkened theater and related the following encounter with what she felt was the spirit of Catherine Bonifas.

"I often come here at night to work on costumes," she began. "I sometimes stay until one or two in the morning. I remember it was late August. We had had thunderstorms all that day and heat lightning reflected on the door as I turned the key to the building that night.

"It was tomb-silent. Although I turned on all the lights, for some reason it seemed darker than usual. Moreover, it was cold, which was unusual, especially at that time of the year. I was working in the gallery that night, cutting out patterns. I remember that as I cut along a line, my fingers felt as though they were wrapped in ice. I was becoming tense from the cold and the fact that my scissors kept disappearing. I would put them down next to where I was working, reach for them and they were not there. They would reappear on a table a few feet away, or on the seat of a chair. I started to doubt my memory and sanity.

"This happened so often that I finally said out loud, 'OK, I am putting my scissors right here.' I emphasized the word 'my.' When I returned they were gone again. The hair on my neck stood straight on end. Goose bumps covered my arms. My quick glance around found the scissors on the floor next to a box of material.

"I left everything where it was. I no longer work alone at night. Sometimes, I know there is definitely something here. What it is or who it is doesn't matter."

Ernestine, a cast member in the current production, then joined us.

"Something happened to me just last night," she said breathlessly. "I was waiting for my cue to go onstage when ice cold air and the smell of talcum powder surrounded me. I remember thinking, God, it's cold. I asked the gal next to me, 'Do you smell that?'

'Smell what?' she answered.

'Talcum powder,' I said.

'No,' she answered.

"Just as suddenly as the cold and fragrance appeared, they were gone. Now tell me, what was that all about? Lots of other stuff has been happening too. We have lost an entire costume, a mutton-

Center stage of the theater. Note orb activity.

sleeved costume along with a veiled hat. And every time we put our gloves down, they disappear only to reappear somewhere else."

I left the two ladies chatting as they made their way up the aisle to the stage. I had discovered during this investigation that one of the hot spots in the theater appeared to be the sound and director's booths located upstairs. One of the sound technicians met me at the top of the stairs, saying, "I believe our ghost likes the director and sound booths. She likes to be in charge. We often see what appears to be a smoky fog drifting across this balcony. Sometimes it get ice-cold up here and often it is only on one side of the booth."

He invited me to sit down. "Although most of us have had encounters with something here at the theater, I never had something I couldn't explain away until I found an old Egyptian-looking necklace laying on a chair in the sound booth. It stayed there until opening night of 'The Fox.' I gave it to one of the young thespians to wear. Everything went wrong during Act One. The muzzle loading rifle wouldn't fire; the starting pistol used for sound effects wouldn't fire. Finally the pin that held the stock together fell out and the barrel fell to the floor with an earth-shattering thud. Lights refused to go on and off at the proper times, costumes disappeared, actors forgot their lines and backstage was chaos.

" 'Find that necklace!' I ordered. We did. And I returned it to the sound booth. The rest of the performance went exceptionally well. Where is the necklace now? It has since disappeared. Catherine will have her fun," he remarked and then continued, "I used to come here alone at night to work in the sound booth. No more. There are sounds, footsteps behind the sets, voices, doors opening and closing, curtains shifting as if by a slight breeze on stage, whispers, and even footsteps on the stairway to the sound booth.

"One night I thought the director was in the sound booth behind me. I heard the door open and close. A frigid sweep of air rushed past me. That's hard to do up there as there are no outside entrances. I turned, expecting to see him, but no one was there. I later saw him and asked if he had been in the sound booth earlier. 'No,' he replied, 'As matter of fact, I just arrived and I'm going up there now. Why?' he questioned. 'Nothing important,' I answered back. *Darn,* I thought to myself, *I just had another run-in with Catherine.*"

I walked slowly down the steps to meet with a previous caretaker, who led me to a rest room where, he had told me earlier, another mysterious happening took place.

"There had been a new lock placed on this door," he said. "In addition, we had just installed a new mirror on the wall. We had to drill holes in the brick wall to get it to hang correctly. The following day, I came in to find it on the floor, smashed into a thousand pieces. Who or what could have pulled that mirror out of a solid brick wall? We have never replaced it in that spot. See here," he pointed. "Here are the holes. I admit I don't believe in ghosts or stuff like that," he said as we made our way through the jungle of props, furniture and unidentifiable stuff, "but I sure don't want to be in here alone anymore.

"You don't have to use my name in this here book you're writing, do ya?" he asked.

"Not if you don't want me to." I answered.

"Well, I never told anyone about the old lady."

We made our way back up to the main floor and into the theater, to the stage.

"I used to clean here. One night I was sweeping the stage and got a weird feeling all over. I looked up and there," he pointed, "right in the front row was an elderly lady with a big hat with a veil wrapped around it. I could tell she was short and a little on the chubby side. She scared the daylights out of me the first time I saw her, but after awhile, I got kinda used to seeing her sitting there. I figured she was one of the cast or crew who just stopped by for some peace and quiet.

"One night I took a break and poured myself a cup of coffee from my thermos. I sat down at the edge of the stage and asked her if she would like some. She never answered. I asked her again, but she never said anything. I thought maybe something was wrong, so I made my way down to the first aisle and walked toward her. She looked right at me and smiled real nice like and then she melted right into the air. Gone. I looked all around but nothing was there. My legs got weak and I spilled my coffee. I got another job the next day. Not many people like working

The sound booth.

here at night."

I looked at the seat he had pointed out to me. There was nothing there. He led me to the front doors and we walked down the steps where I thanked him for his help.

"Just don't use my name, lady," he said as he walked over to his car.

During my interviews at the theater, I had taken three rolls of film with a 35–mm camera and carried along my favorite digital. Not one picture turned out. Each of them had a haze or fog or some sort of distortion. In one, a large halo of light appeared on the center stage curtain. Ghosts are funny this way. They are somewhat shy when it comes to having their picture taken.

My personal encounter with the Catherine's spirit took place just last evening. I had enrolled in a clay-throwing class and discovered I could not, for the life of me, keep the clay centered on the wheel - an absolute must if you want to make a pot. It was suggested I try hand-building. It was fun and I found this was my medium, but in the process, I misplaced a tool called a pin tool.

As the evening wore on, I discovered other members of the class had also misplaced a tool or too. As a matter-of-fact, there was several tools that had gone missing. Some were found in unusual places. I still have not found mine. Catherine just hasn't put it down yet.

Lightning sprinkled across the pavement and followed me to my car as I left the Bonifas Fine Arts Center.

Delft Theater, Escanaba

I repeat – for some reason, ghosts love theaters. This short tale is from a former employee of the Delft who kept his story short, but in this case, not so sweet. The Delft is located on Ludington between Ninth and Tenth Streets.

I followed the projectionist up the stairs to a small room about seven feet by seven feet, with enough room for him to sit down and for a few shelves that would have held the feature films for the week. A small light bulb hung on a string overhead. The room was dim, gloomy, and in utter disarray.

"I used to come here early," he said as he walked through the mess. "Several times I heard footsteps coming up the stairs while I worked. When I checked, there was never anyone there. I often heard whispering in the theater and sometimes coughing. Sometimes a seat would bang like someone pushed it up. Over time I got used to the sounds and pretty much ignored them. I even got used to the moans that came from the back door that leads down to the basement."

He led me back downstairs to the main floor as he continued his story.

"I know there was a story of a young actress who died accidentally back in the early 1900's, shortly after the theater was built," he said. "The story I got was she got tangled in the ropes backstage and accidentally hung herself. Then there's the story of the janitor who broke his neck when he fell down the stairs that go into the basement. I guess he laid there three days before they found him.

"Never bothered me until one night about two years ago, when I came into work and found a coil of rope laying right here," he stopped and pointed, "in front of this door." (The door leads to the upstairs projection room and the balcony that we had just left.) "I knew it wasn't there the night before. I kinda wondered about it as I picked it up. I turned on the lights and went to the back door to put the rope back behind the stage. I went to open the door and it wouldn't budge. I pulled on it and pulled it hard. It wouldn't move. I shouted, 'Whoever you are, let go right now! I need to get in!'

"Suddenly the door opened as easily as if it were on buttered hinges. An ice-cold fog wrapped around me. I quickly tossed the rope through the doorway. The frigid air moved up my neck and down my spine. I slammed the door shut and ran up the aisle to the front of the theater. I had had it. The fogs that used to move across the screen during a film, the curtains swaying on the stage, the lights dimming and then coming on real bright, the voices – all of it. I was done.

"I called my boss and told him I was too sick to work that night. I never went back. Yeah, there's lots of stories about strange happenings in this place. I sure won't ever work here again."

He walked me to the front door, turned and locked it and continued walking down Ludington Street. He never said goodbye. He just left. I turned around and looked at the old billboard frame. I got the creeps just standing there. It turned cloudy and the sky had darkened. It started to drizzle as I walked back to my car.

The Delft is now a popular nightspot on Ludington Street. Naturally, no one will admit to anything supernatural happening in the establishment, although, some of the help admit they will not stay alone after closing, and yes, sometimes some areas on the dance floor and in the ladies rest room get ice cold. So cold that a shiver will spread up your back and make the hair on your neck stand on end.

However, as we all know, winters in the U.P. can cause cold drafts in old buildings.

The Grave Yard Shift, A Railroad Round House near Escanaba

I received the following true story in writing from a fellow YMCA member's husband. Here are his words.

The graveyard shift is the eleven to seven night shift. Many strange things happen that nobody knows about. It is real different than working day shift and the roundhouse at Wells is the worst place to be alone at night. It is worse between two and four a.m., when there is no train out. The building creaks and groans. The rats and mice run around.

No train was out this night and it was a bad weather night. The wind whispered and crawled through the building. My brother Ed had worked the night train with a man called Big Steve. Ed asked me if I would take a pair of chopper mitts from the 102 locomotive to Big Steve, who was in the hospital. Well, I never got around to doing it. Here, the man is real sick and wanting his chopper mitts and I never got around to bringing them. I was thinking about that when I poured myself a cup of coffee.

It was about 3 a.m. when the train usually came in. I was sitting in a chair reading a Reader's Digest. I must have dozed off and dropped the book, which woke me up. All the doors were locked in the roundhouse, but someone had turned on the cab light in the 102 locomotive. I watched a figure walk around the engine compartment. I hollered out, "Who is there?" No answer came. Then the light went out. I squinted to see a figure approach me. The air grew freezing cold. It was Big Steve. I started to get up but I couldn't move. My hair stood straight on end. It felt like my blood turned to ice water. My eyes followed him as he went to the metal side door and walked right through it! I got unfrozen and ran over to the door. It was still bolted shut – on the inside.

I went back and sat down and thought about what had just happened. By this time I was talking out loud to myself, "I know that was Big Steve. Why didn't he stop when I called out? How did he just walk through the door?" I wasn't scared then. Scared came later.

One more thing, my brother Ed came in before my shift was done that morning and told me Big Steve had died around 3 o'clock that morning. Did I tell you he had his chopper mitts in his hand when he walked by me? We checked the 102 and his chopper mitts were gone. Gone to eternity, I figured, along with him.

"Don't Move a House," Manistique

Manistique's history goes back deep into the forests of the Upper Peninsula. Lumber was cut north of here and sent down the Manistique River to Lake Michigan, where it was shipped to other ports as far away as Chicago. Manistique may have exported it's lumber, but it has kept its ghosts.

The house was Leslie's family home, built by her great-great-grandparents, probably in the 1840's. The deed to the property showed the description and ownership of the land, but not the house. They knew it was one of the original homesteads in the village. It had just always been there, according to the locals. No one seemed to know its age, or who had built it. They also were aware of the house's history; that is, the fact that all of the family members who had ever lived in the house had also died in the house.

Leslie and John had the house moved from Manistique to property they owned on a small inland lake nearby. They worked throughout the spring and summer, and finally the house was reassembled on the lot overlooking the blue water.

Walls were re-plastered, floors polished and buffed to their original finish, ceiling cracks fixed and woodwork realigned when strange things began to happen. Leslie began to recall the stories she and her friends had laughed about on sleepovers during stormy nights. Her mother had insisted the house was haunted by an uncle, and by her grandmother and maybe even by Uncle

Harry's wife, Mildred. The uncle had been a carpenter who was very fussy about his tools. He kept them well cleaned and neatly in their place in his workshop. He had died in the house more than twenty years before.

Tools had turned up missing while they were working on the house. John would put a hammer down and go to pick it up, then find it had disappeared. The first few times John thought he had just misplaced it. But time and time again, whatever tool he was working with would turn up missing from where he had put it. It was very frustrating and often maddening for John. One time, a brand new electric sander he was working with disappeared in the middle of refinishing the dining room floor.

After he and Leslie searched the house, car, and property for it, John had to run to town to buy a new one. It turned up four months later when Leslie nearly tripped over it, in the very same room, on the now newly finished floor, exactly where John had originally put it. The uncle may have liked his little tricks but they didn't give John any enjoyment.

They would often catch an apparition moving across the hallway from the children's room to the room where Leslie's mother had died. She appeared as a woman wearing a large victorian-type hat. She looked to be fussing with the veil as she moved silently from one room to the next. Friends often complained of the cold air that seemed to circle them when they came to play cards in the dining room. Too often to be mere circumstance, someone in the party would see a white floating mist in the living room doorway. Even their best friends soon refused to sit alone anywhere in the house, including the bathroom where the door would not stay closed in spite of new locks!

A ghost of a man often appeared on the front porch, just before sunset. He just sat on the steps and as the sun went down, he slowly disappeared into a fine mist that seemed to float upwards.

His appearance gave the family dog a near heart attack on several occasions. The hound no longer sits by the front door, but instead waits for a back door entrance.

Many times upon returning home from town, John and Leslie would catch lights moving from room to room in the house. They would then run upstairs to search for the invaders. Of course, in time, they came to realize they were searching for a different type of visitor.

John and Leslie still live in the house on the lake. They will deny any knowledge of a haunting in their home. After spending a day in their company and interviewing them, I backed my jeep up and started to turn up the driveway when I saw a woman, as plain as day, in an upstairs window. She was wearing a large hat.

I waved goodbye to John and Leslie, who were standing on the front porch steps. Then I looked back at the upstairs window. There was nothing there.

The Haunting of Marble House, Somewhere off US 2

This house is located just off US-2 between the Blaney Park and St. Ignace. Only the owners will recognize this account. They invited me to investigate their home. I did. Historical accounts of the house come from the owners.

On December 4, 1879, Governor David H. Jerome gave the Detroit, Mackinaw & Marquette Railroad Company the right to construct a railroad from the Straits of Mackinaw to Marquette Harbor on Lake Superior and gave all patents on the land to the rail company. The Railroad Company, on July 1, 1880, mortgaged the property and franchises to Frank K. Andersen and John F. McLaskey. These are the first actual names recorded on the abstract of the future home of Marble House.

The property, at that time over 400,000 acres, changed ownership many times through the years. When US-2 was completed as a dirt road in 1882, the house had already been built where it now stands. How it reached its present size and curious room layout is not recorded in the abstract. It is suspected that at one time it was rectangular and was used as a boarding house for employees of the railroad. If the downstairs had been used as a payroll office and the upper floor as a bunkhouse, that may explain the mysterious placement of closets, doorways and spaces where something should be, but are not.

Many people have passed through the old house: railroad

men, loggers, travelers, women, infants, husbands and wives. Many have left their essence behind, an almost palpable energy which could explain the haunting of the old house by its phantom visitors.

Sitting back about a quarter of a mile from the road, the nearly two-hundred-year-old white house is shrouded by tall, dark pines and overgrown cedars. Both back and front porches are typically lengthy with pillars, railings, and wooden steps. On both floors, six tall narrow windows line the front of the house. The window glass is very old. It distorts curtains, sunlight and whatever else may look in or look out. A huge rose bush is directly in front of the front porch steps; you have to walk around it to get to the front door. Many owners and visitors have thought it a strange placement for a rose bush. There is a clearing out back where four huge mound-like islands trail across an open meadow surrounded by thick forest.

The haunting began soon after the young married couple had purchased the old house from the bank. Although it was in desperate need of repair, it was perfect for them with its four bedrooms, five acres of land and reasonable price. Shortly after taking possession of it they began remodeling. They were constantly smelling oil fumes and the power kept going off and on, so their first improvements were the additions of a new furnace and new wiring. The wiring would be an ongoing problem, a problem still unresolved. The lights constantly go on and off. The TV comes on at two in the morning. The radio is turned off by an unseen hand that turns it back on hours later, usually in the middle of the night.

Batteries never last long and new light bulbs are the first items on the shopping list. The old house, in spite of a new heating system and insulation, is never warm.

The furnace worked hard during first winter. Frigid cold spots gathered in the hallways and snaked around their ankles as they moved from room to room. An old brick fireplace pushed more soot into the living room than heat, so using it as a source of warmth was soon forgotten. The winter wind opened and closed doors as frigid air moved freely about the house.

Then in the spring, when the first green shoots of grass peeked through the snow and the stark black branches of maples started to leaf, they started to remodel the kitchen. A wall had to be removed to make room for new appliances. Marvin carefully braced the ceiling. He worked on the kitchen every spare minute.

He was puzzled and surprised when removing a portion of the old kitchen wall revealed another entrance to the stairway to the upstairs. After careful measuring, he knew this way up would be more practical than the current one. As he worked, he felt frigid air sweep past him up the stairway. Seconds later, he felt the icy cold brush past him again.

This happened so frequently that, out of exasperation, he finally asked Lilann to bring him a pair of winter gloves. He kept working and upon finishing, stood back from his work. He was amazed at how it looked as though the stairway had always been there. The doorway to the upstairs was now in the living room instead of smack dab in the middle of the kitchen, where space had been so limited. After several more weeks of work, three new windows with lacy white curtains faced the front porch. An old oak dining room table bought at auction found its home in front of the windows. The front door was replaced with a new insulated one, and Marvin then started to replace the front steps.

While Lilann was baking one sunny afternoon, she felt an uneasy presence behind her. She slowly turned to catch out of the corner of her eye what looked to be an elderly man sitting at the table. The sun shining through the windows often played tricks of light in the kitchen and Lilann thought it was that phenomena again. She walked over to the windows, pulled the shades halfway down and returned to the counter where spoonfuls of cookies sat neatly in rows on a baking sheet.

Again, she felt a presence. She turned fully around and looked directly at the table where he sat watching her. She stared at the ghostly presence as it melted into nothing. She calmly turned back to her baking. Her hands were shaking as she pulled the oven door open and placed the cookies inside. She walked to the front porch and sat in an old rocking chair that had come with the house. She was a little frightened.

The aroma of freshly baked cookies and coffee met Marvin as he stepped on the cement blocks used as steps until he finished the job. He called for Lilann. She was upstairs in the bathroom hanging fresh towels when she felt a soft touch on her shoulder. She turned, expecting to see Marvin, as she had heard the kitchen door close. Instead, there stood the elderly man. She squeaked a small scream and ran from the room to the staircase.

Marvin met her on his way up to answer her scream. She explained the ghostly presence and while they sat drinking coffee in the kitchen, he told her of his own experiences with the old man. He first saw him sitting in the rocking chair on the front porch as he installed the new kitchen windows. At first Marvin thought he was a neighbor but realized he was dealing with something not normal when the apparition dissipated as Marvin reached to shake hands and introduce himself.

Marvin confessed that after this, the man appeared interested in the work Marvin was doing and he often showed up standing on the porch or sitting in the old rocker to watch. Because he didn't want to frighten Lilann, he hadn't told her of the ghostly apparition who turned out to be merely an unobtrusive visitor. Lilann agreed the spirit was not spooky; he just startled her with his sudden appearances. However, she told Marvin, he would not touch her again and she would make sure of it. They both agreed they could live with this spirit who had probably once occupied the old house and obviously missed its surroundings.

Lilann continued to catch glimpses of the old man in the kitchen or through the window on the front porch. Only one more time did he touch her on the shoulder. She was peeling potatoes for dinner when she heard his footsteps on the front steps. Next, she felt his ice-cold touch on her shoulder. She whirled around and shouted, "Don't ever touch me again! Do you hear me? Or you have to leave here forever!"

She and Marvin didn't see or hear the old man for months. His visitations had apparently stopped, until one afternoon she heard footsteps on the porch, as if pacing back and forth, back and forth. This continued sporadically for several weeks until she finally opened the front door and said loudly, "All right. You can come in; however, don't ever touch me again. Is this understood?"

Evidently it was. Once again, the old ghost rejoined them.

Late that fall, Marvin decided to renovate the small back room attached to the living room. He thought it would make a nice office or den. Lilann wanted the room painted but it had been wallpapered in the past, so they began to remove the old wallpaper. To their surprise, they uncovered an old doorway covered with a piece of plasterboard. It had once been a door to the back yard. Marvin recovered it correctly and they cheerfully painted the room a creamy white.

It started at once. Books fell off the shelves; chairs moved from one place to another and the shadow of a huge clock appeared on the wall. Lilann first saw the shadow when she was putting up a wallpaper border near the ceiling. She thought she heard a clock chime. She slowly turned herself as she stood on the ladder, to see where the sound had come from. There it was on the wall - the shadow of a grandfather clock. Lilann got down from the ladder and walked to the wall. She reached out to touch the shadow when suddenly the ladder fell over. On the opposite side of the room, books spewed from the book case. She ran from the room, calling for her husband. They returned to find the books replaced. The shadow was gone. The ladder was upright again.

This became the only room in the house that Lilian refused to enter. She had had enough of books flying across the room at her and the chiming clock. Marvin used the room as an office and den. He spent many winter nights reading in a cozy chair and paid little attention to the behavior of the spirit. The window shades flew up and down, books fell off the shelves and lights flickered on and off. He ignored the entire show and continued whatever task he was doing. He thought it was nonsense and often told the presence to learn how to behave. That seemed to quiet this particular spirit down for lengthy periods.

As the days grew shorter and night stole the daylight ever earlier, Lilann and Marvin often discussed the ghosts that lived with them. They had not become used to their presence, but they learned to accept them because they loved their home and its location. Lilann believed the old man not only missed his home but also his wife. She continued to feel his presence in the kitchen and once in while she would catch a glimpse of him sitting at the table watching her as she prepared meals.

There were two ghosts haunting their house, neither frightened them. As long as Lilann stayed away from Marvin's den, she was comfortable sharing her home with the old man whose appearances were becoming less frequent.

It was the deep middle of winter, when snowdrifts covered roads and storms were relentless as they moved across the peninsula. The lakes froze tight, as did most of the pipes in the old house. Marvin, Lilann and the local plumber were frantically busy trying to locate leaks that allowed icy water to drip from the kitchen ceiling, to create frozen stains in the living room and icy streams in the bathrooms. After two weeks of relentless pursuit and damage control, the leaks were brought under control. The house even felt somewhat warmer. That was before the third ghost made itself known.

Lilann liked to hang her clothes up in the backyard. Even in the winter months, she would carry a basket full of sheets to hang on the back clotheslines that Marvin had placed behind the house near the old apple orchard. One morning in early February, Marvin's work sent him to St. Ignace, so Lilann, after taking care of household chores, looked forward to having the whole day to herself without interruption.

Sunlight poured through the laundry room windows as she finished the wash. She took the sheets out to hang on the line while the dryer took care of the rest. She put on her fur-lined jacket and gloves and walked around the corner of the house to the clotheslines. As soon as she entered the backyard, she felt uneasy. She noticed that black clouds, harbingers of snow, had gathered in the north. The wind had picked up, forming small tornadoes in the snow. She pulled the first sheet, steaming from the cold, out of the basket and flipped it over the line when she smelled something so rotten she gasped to catch her breath.

As she tugged at the sheet to straighten it, the steam had formed the apparition of a tall woman dressed in black. Lilian's heart stopped. The putrid smell of rotting flesh surrounded her as a frigid wind pushed her backwards. Nearly frozen with fear, she forced herself to run to the house. Slamming the door behind her, she backed up to the kitchen sink. Her glove-covered hands clutched at the edge of the countertop. She listened. Silence. She edged over to the table to look out the window. The porch was empty. The smell warned Lilann of the woman's ghostly approach. Lilann covered her scream with her hands. The smell slowly dissipated. She waited... her breathing shallow with fear. Her heart slammed against her chest as she clutched the car keys from the counter and walked cautiously to the front door.

She stood on the porch, gathering her courage to make a run for the car parked not fifteen feet away in the driveway. The sun had disappeared into a curtain of heavy snow. The squall could last for minutes or for the rest of the day. She didn't dare leave the house. She returned to the kitchen and remained there until Marvin returned that evening to find her asleep at the kitchen table still wearing her winter jacket and gloves. The house was frigid.

The putrid smell always predicted the nearby presence of this particular ghost who had, so far, only appeared outside of the old house. A psychic once told them that the spirit had lost her way. Her name was Rose. Perhaps, Lilann thought, she had planted the huge rose bush in the middle of the front steps.

It was their second summer at Marble House when Lilann's sister, Bridget, came for a visit with her three-year-old son, Tommy. Lilann had told Bridget stories of the spirits they had inherited when they bought the house. Bridget thought it was Lilann's imagination until she encountered the newest addition to the family.

Bridget was sound asleep in an upstairs bedroom at the top of the stairs, just down the hall from Lilann and Marvin's room. It had been raining. The wind had switched to the north through the night, causing the lace curtains next to the bed to sway. A cold breeze brushed over Bridget's shoulders as she turned to catch up the blankets, but instead of the blanket, Bridget touched something as cold as death. She awoke with a start. There, sitting on the bed, was a young boy, about ten or so. He stood up and moved to the door. Bridget stared. He moved from sight. Bridget felt her pulse in her ears as she waited for the dream to pass. Instead, he appeared again, in the doorway. He glowed somewhat as he looked down the hall toward her son's room. He again moved from sight.

This time Bridget grew worried about Tommy. She ran to the doorway to glimpse the spirit entering the small bedroom. She ran to the room and found her boy in a fit of coughing. He was soaking wet and so were his covers. She grabbed him and ran down the hallway to Lilann and Marvin's room. She woke them as she carried Tommy to their bed. Marvin discovered the window was wide open in the little boy's room and rain had soaked the curtains and bed. Lilann and Bridget changed the little boy and cuddled him back to sleep. He smiled as he fell back to sleep, murmuring that he had met his guardian angel.

Indeed, and so he had, for not a week later, again the young angel appeared. It happened as Marvin was in the backyard trimming the apple trees. The strange ten-year-old again appeared and beckoned him to the front yard. *Tommy,* he thought, as he ran down the driveway in time to grab the boy before he ran onto the highway after a stray cat.

By this time, Bridget was ready to cut her visit short. With Tommy firmly buckled into the back seat, she hugged her sister and her brother-in-law goodbye. She encouraged them to leave and find another place to call home. As Bridget followed the drive to the highway, from her rearview mirror she saw a woman in the side yard. *A neighbor,* she thought as she turned to follow US-2 to the bridge.

Yes, there were four of them. Four ghosts. After Bridget and Tommy's departure, Marvin and Lilann finally agreed they would sell the house and look for one without all of the "extras." Marvin made an appointment with a realtor who on entering the house, asked if the elderly gentleman on the front porch would like to join them. That ensured their decision to leave the house immediately.

The house was sold. And sold again. And again.

Several seasons have passed since my encounter with the owners of Marble House. My travels often take me near the old place. Today an abandoned "For Sale" sign remains posted near the end of the circle driveway. The lace curtains are gone from the windows; the path to the front door is overgrown with weeds.

The only sign that the house is still inhabited is the vacant rocker rocking gently on the front porch.

All houses wherein men have lived
and died are haunted houses.

Through the open doors the harmless
phantoms on their errands glide with feet
that make no sounds upon the floors.

~ Henry Wadsworth Longfellow (1807-1882)

Off the Beaten Track

The following is a collection of mysterious tales included for the reader's delectation.

Bark River

When Kathy and Jim Dawson purchased the old homestead built in 1933, they had no idea that along with the house and barn, they also got a ghost. When they started to remodel the kitchen in the old home, they began to hear heavy footsteps coming from upstairs.

"...Like an old woman wearing those black shoes with big heels, like my grandma used to wear," said Kathy. Kathy explained how the footsteps would pace back and forth, back and forth, going right through the walls from one room to the next.

"And then, when we were upstairs, we heard noises in downstairs," said Jim. "Sounds like something heavy being dropped or furniture being pushed across the floor." They never heard anything from the attic. It was just an empty attic. However, the basement was another story. Noises filtered up through the registers of the house at all times of the day and night. It was more than just the old place settling. Bubbling, gurgling, and banging often filled the house like a first-class stereo system.

In late summer, after finishing the kitchen, they tore up the old carpeting in the living room, dining room, hallway, and two downstairs bedrooms. They discovered hardwood, bird's-eye maple floors throughout. They also discovered the activity of their spirit increased. Kathy, out of the corner of her eye, would glimpse shadows moving along the walls.

"I thought it might be a bird flying by a window, but the same thing would happen when I wasn't near a window. The water would run in all the faucets downstairs. I would shut them all off. Then I would hear them running upstairs. Before I could reach the top step, they stopped."

The smells of fresh baked goods frequently permeated the entire house.

Jim laughed quietly, "The nearest bakery is nine miles down the road…and it's been closed for years." He shook his head in disbelief and added, "I couldn't keep flashlight batteries. Every time I put in new batteries, they worked for a few minutes and then they were done. I bought new flashlights. Same thing. The batteries were drained of power within minutes."

"We finally got in touch with the old owner of the house. He told us he and his mother had believed the house was haunted, but were afraid to say anything because they needed to sell it."

The spirit never harmed them nor really frightened them and they often referred to it as the "family ghost."

However, finally, after another sleepless night, Jim agreed to have the house blessed prior to building on an addition.

Since that time, Kathy said, the activity has slowed a bit. Once in awhile, she admits to walking through an icy cold spot or smelling toast long after Jim has left for work. And, she takes a deep breath before continuing, they have recently noticed some problems in the new addition. The same windowpane has cracked three times so far and a large slate tile has cracked in the same place several times. And still, she often senses the presence of an older woman. She believes whomever she is returns to see if they are taking care of the house.

As we finished our last conversation, Kathy watched her two cats acting strangely.

"What is the matter with these darn cats? I have never seen them act like this before!"

I watched as the two tiger cats acted like they were rubbing themselves against an invisible companion. They slowly disappeared around the corner of the kitchen doorway. An icy cold draft followed them as they meowed their way past me.

Kathy looked at me strangely and asked, "Do you smell toast?"

Cut River Bridge Area

The young waitress who worked the early shift in a restaurant along US-2 snapped her gum as she told me the following tale. It seems the haunting of this particular place could be blamed entirely on the owners, who told her they had made a deal with an elderly guy to park his pick-up camper behind the restaurant and use their restroom in the mornings if he would make coffee for the early shift. This arrangement worked for several years until one snowy morning, when two of the waitresses found the old man lying on the kitchen floor. He had died of a heart attack.

To this day; not every day, but on some days; an early morning waitress will arrive to find the coffee perking away. Frequently, members of the early morning shift watch the apparition of an elderly man making coffee. Because help is hard to find in these remote parts of the U.P., the new owners don't want to scare away any future help so they have asked me not to identify the location of this haunting.

Coffee anyone?

M 28, between Newberry and Munising

I have received many reports of mysterious happenings throughout the U.P. Several have been about UFO activity. These sightings were more frequent when our two U.P. airbases were active, but occasional sightings still continue to occur. One of the more recent reports of an unusual sighting took place along the so-called Seney Stretch, located between Munising and Seney on M-28.

The following story was reported to a local radio station by two different travelers who reported seeing the same phenomena as they drove down this long stretch of highway.

It was around 11 a.m. The morning was filled with sunshine and blue autumn sky. George and Sharon Anderson were returning from an overnight trip to a local casino.

"What's that?" asked Sharon, as she pointed out the front window of the car. "Oh my God, George! What is that?" she cried out. It looked like a solid black object floating just above the tree line in front of them on the right hand side of the highway. George slowed the car. It was now almost directly above them. As it passed silently over the car, they could see it was as big as a garage and solid black. It was flat, as if it were standing on end, and it had four points, somewhat like a shield.

George stopped the car. They both got out to get a better look, but by the time George had pulled over and stopped, it was gone. Later that day they discovered several other travelers had seen the same object that morning. On arriving home that afternoon, they called the nearest airports. Their calls verified there was no air traffic at the time in that area, and apparently, others had also called the local radio stations to report the same sighting that morning.

Did you see it?

The End of Cemetery Road, Powers

Charlie attended an old country school that held about forty kids back in the early '50's. Most of the kids he grew up with rode the aged yellow school bus that traveled up and down the old two-track lanes of the county. One of the stops they made was on a dead-end road just past an old cemetery, where a strange house sat at the edge of a vast tangle of woods and marsh. It was a strange house because it was very clean and neat and had a fresh coat of paint every few years. Bright blue shutters and a bright pink door graced the long front porch. However, the back end of the house was in shambles. The tar-papered roof was partially gone and the windows sagged with bits of splintered glass that clung to the morning dew.

Every school day, the bus stopped there to pick up two boys who were about three years younger than Charlie. When you are a kid, you really don't notice a lot of the background stuff in your life, but as you grow up you begin to notice things – like that house.

After a few years, Charlie's curiosity finally got the better of him, and he asked the two boys, "Why don't your folks fix up the back end of your house?"

The older boy replied, "The ghosts won't let us." He hung his head as he continued, "I'll punch your lights out if you tell anyone else or if you make fun of me and my brother. You promise not to?"

Charlie pledged he wouldn't, and crossed his heart and hoped to die. The boy nodded his head, pulled Charlie close to him and whispered, "The last time our mom and dad tried to fix up the other end, the ghosts moved into our side of the house. They moved furniture all night long, rang bells, opened doors, flushed toilets and darn near scared the dog right outa his tail! Window curtains floated, mom's cooking burned, windows opened and, worst of all, dad's Sunday hat went sailing into the front yard! Since then, we leave the back end of the house alone and they leave us alone."

Charlie was flabbergasted. He watched through the dirty bus

window as the boys walked down the long driveway to their house. As the bus pulled away, he looked carefully at the back of the house. He wondered who the ghosts were. Charlie never told a soul about that conversation. He made darn sure he never went down that road alone, even when he was dating the younger sister of the boys he talked to that day when he was in the eighth grade. Frankly, he told me, he was always a little scared of her.

To this day, that house still sits near the edge of the woods at the end of the cemetery road and the back is still in shambles.

Stella, Menominee

There is a bar in Menominee with a ghost given the name of Stella. Patrons often hear her pacing up and down the upstairs hallway, opening and closing doors as she goes from one room to the next. She was seen once by some regular old-timers who occupy the chrome barstools while exchanging the gossip of the day. She scared the daylights out of them when she appeared from the back room one gloomy afternoon wearing a Victorian-like gown and white veil. According to the group she literally floated out the front door.

A cleaning woman claims to have seen her once in an upstairs window. She sometimes is heard moving furniture that isn't there anymore, as the upstairs has been vacant for the past twenty years. The patrons claim they have heard the sound of a woman's sweet voice, singing softly, coming from the old heat registers that line the bar. Although there haven't been curtains on the windows since the new owner bought the place, people tell him they can see curtains fluttering in the breeze.

At least, they think it is curtains.

Somewhere in the South-Central U.P.

The nursing home had been recently expanded when strange things began to happen. Although the old building is now locked and vacant, lights continue to go off and on and the elevators continue to go up and down. In spite of thorough investigations by the local power company, no explanation has been found for the frequent mischief taking place in the old complex.

On the third floor of the newly renovated area, across from the nurse's station, is the medicine room. The top half of the door has a window. Through it, nurses often catch movement in that room from the corner of their eye. When they check, nothing is there but an icy fog that lingers and then dissipates as they leave the room. Is it a trick of their imagination? Not according to many of the nurses I have interviewed who have worked there.

They also claim to have seen a woman in a blue robe walk down the hallway next to the medicine room. She goes all the way down to the elevator, then disappears into nothing. Some have followed her but have found that same icy fog clinging to the area. They quickly retreat to the safety of the nurses' station.

Some of the staff describe what appears to be a nurse wearing a uniform of the early 1930's, complete with a short cape and the winged cap of a registered nurse. This spirit walks by the nurse's station, leaving a trail of ice cold air behind her, as she turns the corner leading to the kitchen. Those who have followed her have found the swinging doors to the kitchen still moving.

The shadowy form of an elderly woman in a wheel chair, with a sleeping cat on her lap, was caught on the second floor by a security camera. This is fine except for the fact there are no wheelchair patients on the second floor nor any patients with a cat. According to one of the nurses who continues on staff, the paranormal activity seems to have slowed in the past two years.

It's a Dog's Life, Stonington Peninsula

There is a log home near the end of the peninsula that has a basement with a dirt floor; the walls are lined with rocks. The owners have two Jack Russell terriers that continually bark and scratch at one corner of the basement to the point where their paws will bleed if their owners do not stop them. The owners have dug up that corner, but found nothing. The dogs continue their strange behavior if allowed in the basement.

Did the owner dig deep enough?

Angel Lake, Newberry

Angel Lake is located north of Newberry. Stories have been told that back in the late 1800's, when it was unacceptable for a young woman to give birth out of wedlock, a woman would be hidden away in the later months of pregnancy. The family would tell stories of an illness or that their daughter was off visiting a sick aunt. When the young women gave birth, the newborns were thrown into the lake. Legend has it that the lake has become haunted by all of the young souls lost so tragically. If you sit quietly by the shoreline, you can almost hear the cries of the lost babies of Angel Lake. To this day you can feel drastic temperature changes near its shoreline.

Care to go for a picnic?

The Last Ghost Story

I returned to Seul Choix Point Lighthouse once again to breathe in the ambience of the place. I loved the smell of dusty warm heat from the sun that filtering through the windows and the fresh smell of the newly waxed floors. The members of the historical society had recently finished their annual spring cleaning and, of course, had several encounters with Captain Townshend. This isn't an unusual occurrence, as it is well known the Captain doesn't like being disturbed after the long, quiet, winter months.

I sat on the back porch, thinking of the story that Dee, one of the tourist guides, had just told me. She had been in the kitchen, washing the floor on her hands and knees, when she heard footsteps on the stairs. She wasn't bothered at first. Then she remembered that Grandma had knocked on the kitchen window as she passed to go for lunch. Only she and Grandma had been in the lighthouse that morning. So if Grandma wasn't there, then whose footsteps did she hear on the stairway?

She hesitantly called out, "Who's there?" Silence. "Grandma, is that you?" Silence.

The footsteps continued down the stairway. One – then another, then – another. Dee gave up waiting to see what would come around the corner and down the hall. She bolted to the back door and ran down the back porch, across the lawn to the gift shop.

"Gee whiz, what's with you Dee?" asked Grandma, as she stood near the screen door.

A woman wearing a bonnet appears in the window. This is impossible because this window is 5 feet above the stairway landing.

"Don't you ever leave me alone in that place again!" cried Dee.

I pondered her story and wished Hank were here to tell me about his latest encounter with our spirit. Hank and Judy were also tour guides for the lighthouse. Apparently, he had been up on the ladder in the dining room, replacing light bulbs in the chandelier as Judy handed them up to him. He was having problems with one of the sockets as he and Judy talked about the upcoming tourist season. He held his hand out for another bulb and felt a piercing cold object placed in his hand. He looked at it. It was a light bulb, but Judy wasn't there to hand it to him. The ladder started to shake as he slowly climbed down and walked purposefully to the side door without glancing up. He walked to the gift shop and sat on a chair in the video room.

Who had handed the light bulb to him? It sure wasn't Judy. She had gone into the parlor to get another pack of light bulbs and then walked out to her car to retrieve their lunches.

I left the bench and walked out on the lawn from where I could see the light tower. It stood glistening white against the blue sky. I remembered the complaints tourists had made to some of the guides last summer about the cigar smoke in the tower. Complaints didn't stop the cigar smoke. After all, it is the

Captain's lighthouse, and he does love his cigars.

I have discovered in my research these past three years, that spirits, like the Captain, do not like change of any kind. Many hauntings begin when an establishment is remodeled. Walls, cupboards or doorways that are moved can cause a shift in normal traffic patterns.

Better think twice before you change the carpeting, select a new tile floor for your kitchen or bath, or change the plumbing or wiring. You inherit your Aunt Mary's house and with your decorating skills you change the living room into a den. Bingo! Aunt Mary is pacing the floor.

A building, formerly a home, is changed into a restaurant and guess what comes to dinner? If former owners were neat housekeepers and the new family is not so dedicated, a spirit may let them know that they are not happy by moving objects, slamming doors, and generally making things, "go bump in the night."

If you think you may have a spirit in your house, there are several ways to know for sure. Ask yourself the following questions: Have you ever caught a movement, a shadow, out of the corner of your eye in a darkened hallway, basement, or bedroom? Have you heard footsteps or rustling sounds on the floor above you or next to you? Have doors or windows opened or closed without human help? Have you put something down and returned to find it gone? Have things like a comb, a jar, a paper or a book been moved?

Have you experienced any smells, like perfume, cigar or cigarette smoke, baking bread, spearmint gum, after-shave lotion, that you cannot explain? Has the TV or radio ever come on without your help? Does one song keep playing every time you tune in your radio station? Do batteries lose their charge? Do you have a feeling of being watched or that you are not alone?

Have you ever encountered icy cold spots or felt a large push of cold air?

How are your photography skills? Do your pictures have fogs in them, unexplained lights or orbs, shadows? How are your pets? Do they refuse to enter a room? Do they play with an unseen playmate? And your mirrors… anything in them? Someone you used to know?

If several of your answers are "yes," then you might consider researching the history of the place where these things have occurred. Most spirits return because they were happy in this place, others return to finish business and still others, like our friend in Sault St. Marie, just do not realize that they are no longer among the living. Remember that spirits are not evil, only people are. Perhaps they are mirrors into the afterlife.

I hope you have enjoyed this Ghostly Road Trip. Perhaps we can do another one someday to uncover other spirits that remain buried in Michigan's Upper Peninsula.

If a candle flame turns blue, a ghost is near to you.

Janice Langley, author and illustrator, was born in Harbor Beach, Michigan, located on the shores of Lake Huron. She grew up with the sound of the Harbor Beach light's fog horn in the background. She is the mother of three grown children and the wife of Richard J. Langley. They reside in Escanaba. You may contact the author at www.thecaptianandharry.com

Also Available by Jan Langley
Books for Children

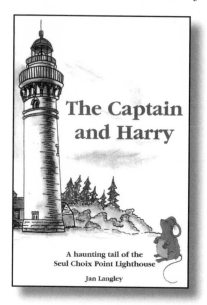
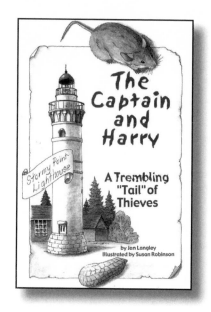

The Captain and Harry, and
The Captain and Harry, A Trembling "Tail" of Thieves

This Children's book series is set at Seul Choix Lighthouse, known as "the Haunted Lighthouse" near Gulliver in the Upper Peninsula of Michigan

The Captain and Harry series are stories of eternal friendship wrapped in historical facts and actual documented spirit sightings in and around the Seul Choix Pointe Lighthouse located in Gulliver, Michigan.

The first story, The Captain and Harry, a haunting tail of the Seul Choix Pointe Lighthouse, begins the series by introducing the two main characters and sets the background for the stories that follow. Lighthouse keeper from 1901-1910 Captain Joseph Townshend's spirit is said to haunt the restored lighthouse.

Captain Townshend and Harry, a very fat field mouse, combine to create characters that are mysterious and lovable.